There are six new HORIZON CARAVEL BOOKS published each year. The titles now available are:

THE UNIVERSE OF GALILEO AND NEWTON	JOAN OF ARC
THE VIKINGS	EXPLORATION OF AFRICA
MARCO POLO'S ADVENTURES IN CHINA	NELSON AND THE AGE OF FIGHTING SAIL
SHAKESPEARE'S ENGLAND	ALEXANDER THE GREAT
CAPTAIN COOK AND THE SOUTH PACIFIC	RUSSIA UNDER THE CZARS
THE SEARCH FOR EARLY MAN	HEROES OF POLAR EXPLORATION
KNIGHTS OF THE CRUSADES	

American Heritage also publishes AMERICAN HERITAGE JUNIOR LIBRARY books, a similar series on American history. The titles now available are:

AIR WAR AGAINST HITLER'S GERMANY	GREAT DAYS OF THE CIRCUS
IRONCLADS OF THE CIVIL WAR	STEAMBOATS ON THE MISSISSIPPI
THE ERIE CANAL	COWBOYS AND CATTLE COUNTRY
THE MANY WORLDS OF BENJAMIN FRANKLIN	TEXAS AND THE WAR WITH MEXICO
COMMODORE PERRY IN JAPAN	THE PILGRIMS AND PLYMOUTH COLONY
THE BATTLE OF GETTYSBURG	THE CALIFORNIA GOLD RUSH
ANDREW JACKSON, SOLDIER AND STATESMAN	PIRATES OF THE SPANISH MAIN
ADVENTURES IN THE WILDERNESS	TRAPPERS AND MOUNTAIN MEN
LEXINGTON, CONCORD AND BUNKER HILL	MEN OF SCIENCE AND INVENTION
CLIPPER SHIPS AND CAPTAINS	NAVAL BATTLES AND HEROES
D-DAY, THE INVASION OF EUROPE	THOMAS JEFFERSON AND HIS WORLD
WESTWARD ON THE OREGON TRAIL	DISCOVERERS OF THE NEW WORLD
THE FRENCH AND INDIAN WARS	RAILROADS IN THE DAYS OF STEAM
INDIANS OF THE PLAINS	

A HORIZON CARAVEL BOOK

THE UNIVERSE OF
GALILEO AND NEWTON

By the Editors of
HORIZON MAGAZINE

Author
WILLIAM BIXBY

Consultant
GIORGIO DE SANTILLANA
Professor of the History and Philosophy of Science
Massachusetts Institute of Technology

ILLUSTRATED WITH PAINTINGS, DRAWINGS,
AND DOCUMENTS, MANY OF THE PERIOD

Published by American Heritage Publishing Co., Inc.
Book Trade and Institutional Distribution by
Harper & Row

FIRST EDITION
Library of Congress Catalogue Number: 64–20204
© 1964 by American Heritage Publishing Co., Inc., 551 Fifth Avenue, New York 17,
New York. All rights reserved under Berne and Pan-American Copyright Conventions.
Trademark CARAVEL registered United States Patent Office

Galileo Galilei (1564–1642)

FOREWORD

Galileo Galilei and Isaac Newton are remembered because of one story about each of them that is unforgettable, though inaccurate. Galileo is seen poised against the uppermost railing of the leaning tower of Pisa, in the act of dropping two different-sized stone weights. Young Newton is visualized beneath his apple tree, unaware of the apple that is about to rap his head and change his life forever.

Although neither picture conforms to historical reality, both are true in the way of legends. For Galileo was indeed a ceaseless experimenter whose inquiries into motion, light, and the organization of the solar system awakened men of his time to the possibility of viewing the universe scientifically. And Newton was apparently inspired by a falling apple to carry on Galileo's work, to formulate the one great law that explains the working of the universe, and thus to lay the foundations for modern science.

Italy at the time of Galileo's birth was basking in the last rays of the Renaissance—that brilliant revival of interest in learning and the arts that is reflected in many of the paintings in this book. It was as if Galileo had come along in that twilight to point Western thought in a new direction, toward science.

Then, in the very year of Galileo's death (1642), Isaac Newton was born in England. By his genius he inaugurated a new age of scientific and mechanical achievement that is also made vivid in illustrations on the following pages.

The relationship between these very different personalities is therefore like that of two complementary stages of a rocket. Galileo, the argumentative "wrangler" who demanded that the universe be examined through a telescope rather than by means of a philosophy book, provided the first lift-off; and Newton, the secretive mathematician who searched among his notes to find a mislaid proof for universal gravitation, put the world into orbit. To both of them, for their description of a clockwork universe that must be probed to be understood, modern scientists are indebted as to few other men of history.

THE EDITORS

Sir Isaac Newton (1642–1727)

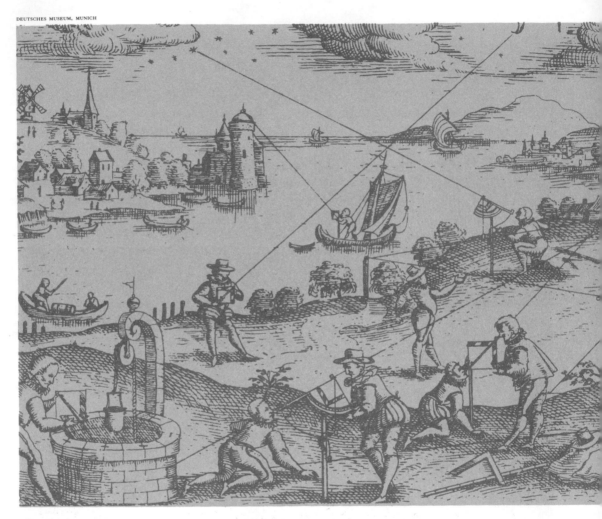

In sixteenth-century Europe, astronomy suddenly became a popular pursuit for gentlemen.

COVER: *This system of interlocking spheres is a model of the universe circa 1597.*
FRONT ENDSHEET: *In an effort to make order of all the stars in the universe, medieval artists pictured them in constellations representing mythological beasts and heroes.*
TITLE PAGE: *A woodcut of the 1400's depicts scholars measuring stellar inclinations.*
BACK ENDSHEET: *In our galaxy are myriad suns and gas islands like this whirlpool nebula.*

CONTENTS

I

THE WRANGLER

Inside the cathedral of Pisa, Italy, on a Sunday morning in 1581, the congregation was kneeling in prayer. Their mumbled, whispered words were the only sounds to be heard in that tall and richly ornamented chamber. It was dark there, for the sun had barely risen; only a little daylight filtered through the narrow windows and fell across the rows of bowed heads.

A monk moved about, silently lighting candles. As he touched each wick with the tip of his torch, another flame arose and cast flickering patterns against the dark walls. When he came to the great chandelier that hung from the coffered ceiling, he reached out and drew it toward him with a long pole. Having lighted the lamp, he released it, and it began swinging freely back and forth, sweeping its radiance over the stone floor like a fast-moving sun.

A young man with reddish hair and blue eyes, aware of the moving light, raised his head to gaze at the lamp. He watched its motions idly at first, then with mounting excitement; his thoughts raced ahead faster as the lamp gradually slowed down. Soon he was staring transfixed, unmindful now of the chanting priest, the swirls of incense, or the ringing of the sonorous brass bell. A hundred questions crowded his thoughts as he held his gaze on the movement of the lamp.

He observed that when it was first set to swinging, it moved swiftly through the darkness, and each swing, back and forth, covered a great distance. Then this distance gradually decreased, and, surprisingly, the speed of the lamp also seemed less.

Was the lamp really slowing down? the young man wondered. Possibly the time of each complete swing—

Galileo discovered the principle of the pendulum by watching an ornate chandelier (above) as it swung beneath the ceiling of Pisa's cathedral (left).

whether it was a long or short movement—was always the same. The only way the young man could know for certain was by timing the motions. He had no timepiece, but he instinctively clapped one hand to his other wrist and compared the regular beats of his pulse to the time it took for the lamp to swing back and forth in ever-decreasing arcs. As nearly as he could determine, by knowing the rate of his pulse, each swing took the same length of time.

The mass was over. The young man, whose name was Galileo, and who was then only seventeen, joined the other worshipers filing slowly from the church. He returned to the University of Pisa, where he was, at his father's insistence, a student of medicine. Back in his room, spurred by the memory of what he had seen, he performed a series of experiments. He tied a heavy weight to the end of a strand of cord, making a simple pendulum. Then, setting the pendulum in motion, he measured the time of each swing against the beat of his pulse. He did this repeatedly until he was certain his supposition was correct; because the rate of speed differed, each progressively shorter swing took the same time.

Galileo had discovered what is known today as the law of the simple pendulum: the swing of a pendulum may be long or short; but as long as it swings, it invariably measures the same amount of time. The only way to cause a change in the time of each swing is to change the length of the pendulum itself.

Being nearly penniless at the university, young Galileo used his discovery to earn some money. He worked out a timing device to sell to doctors in Pisa. It was a simple string pendulum of variable length. A doctor could adjust the length of the pendulum so that its swing coincided with a patient's pulse rate. On a subsequent day, when a doctor took another reading, he could compare the two rates and get an accurate account of how his patient was progressing.

From Galileo's discovery of the principle of the pendulum, a totally new concept of the design of timepieces evolved. But what proved even more significant than the discovery itself was his method of arriving at it—a system that today is called the scientific method.

Galileo was, to begin with, instinctively and intensely curious; nothing in nature or in the world around him was too commonplace to escape his notice. Also, he possessed the imagination to guess the principle behind the phenomenon he had observed. And finally, he had the patience

Pisa, whose position astride the Arno River is seen in the 1649 view below, was one of the great mercantile cities of Italy in the twelfth century. But by the time of Galileo's birth, it had lost battles and business to Florence. Pisa's famous building, the leaning tower (No. 3, at top, left), was originally built to stand upright.

TEXT CONTINUED ON PAGE 16

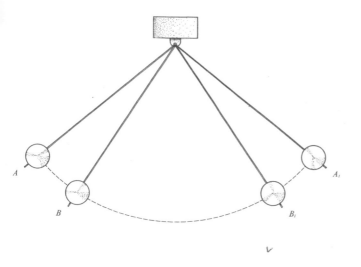

Porta Lucana.

1. Templ. S. Stephani.
2. Basilica Princeps.
3. Campanile.
4. S. Iohannis.
5. Campus Sanctus.
6. M. Ducis Palatium.
7. Hortus Medicus.
8. Naualia.
9. Castellum.
10. Archiepiscopi ædes.
11. Xenodochium.
12. Laspina.
13. S. Lorenzo.
14. S. Francesco.
15. S. Siluestro.
16. El Carmine.
17. S. Antonio.

FIUME

N.Y. PUBLIC LIBRARY, RARE BOOK DIVISION

Galileo was thirty-eight when the likeness above was drawn—the earliest-known portrait. By then he had perfected the application of the pendulum principle to clocks. That principle, as diagramed at left above, is that a swinging ball on the end of a string will cover the distance between A and A-1 in the same length of time as it will the distance between B and B-1.

13

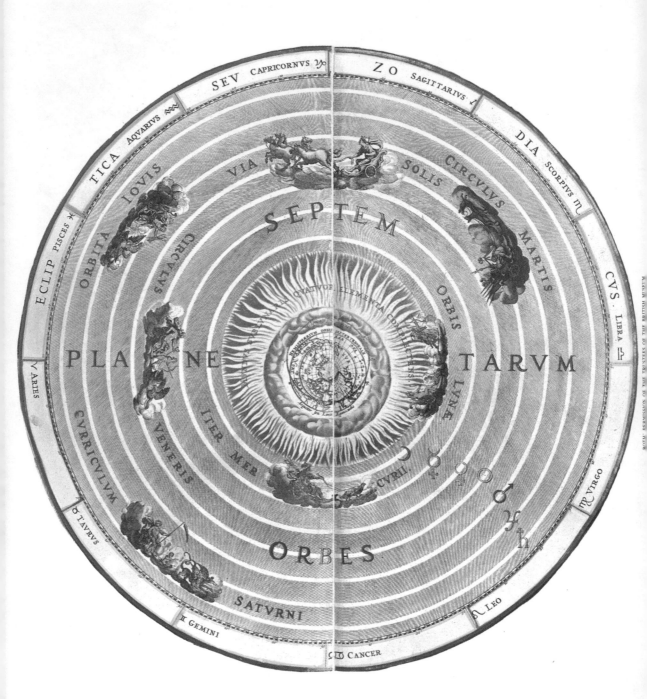

In 1660, almost twenty years after Galileo's death, these colorful and conflicting charts of the heavens were engraved by Andreas Cellarius. The one above shows a cross section of the spherical universe in which Aristotle and most other ancients believed. The earth is in the center, surrounded by concentric, glasslike spheres on which the sun, the moon, and the other planets revolve. There is also a final, distant sphere for the stars.

Without stating whether it was correct, Cellarius also portrayed the universe described by the sixteenth-century Polish astronomer Copernicus and accepted by Galileo. This engraving shows the sun at the center, with Mercury, Venus, and the earth in circular orbits around it. Beyond the earth are the other planets that can be seen with the naked eye: Mars, Jupiter, and Saturn. Earth and Jupiter have moons in orbit about them.

15

TEXT CONTINUED FROM PAGE 12

and the conviction to check his guess by repeated experiments. When in later life he raised his sights from the curiosities of the everyday world to the sky above him, using this powerful scientific method, he was able to reveal something of the long-hidden nature of the solar system.

Many of his theories were not new, and many of them were not entirely correct; almost none of them were accepted by his contemporaries. Through most of his life, Galileo was considered either a crank or a heretic, sometimes both. But though most scholars and clerics of his day opposed him, many men of science found something of value in what he claimed to have proved. He died in disgrace, but his work and that of his successors perpetuated his memory. One of these, the Englishman Isaac Newton, later advanced a theory powerful enough to define the structure of the entire universe. However, without the groundwork laid by Galileo, Newton's work might not have been possible. Newton scaled a great peak in solving the mystery of the heavens, but he did so with a strong and reliable assist from Galileo.

A carving on the bell tower of the cathedral in Florence shows Aristotle (holding book) arguing with his tutor Plato. The two ancient Greeks were venerated almost as saints in the two centuries before Galileo's birth, during that great revival of interest in classical learning known as the Renaissance.

CAMPANILE DEL DUOMO, FLORENCE: PHOTO ALINARI

Aristotle's scientific teachings had entered medieval Europe by way of the great library at Alexandria and through Arab scholars. Thus, the "computist" seated at right in this thirteenth-century miniature holds a book with Arab script. The astronomer observing stars with a primitive astrolabe appears to be reading figures to a scribe. In his right hand the astronomer has a tube that is a simple telescope.

Even as a young man, Galileo's ideas about nature were so revolutionary that they earned him enemies among teachers and fellow students at the university and among the priests of his church. To them, Galileo seemed rigidly determined to upset all the accepted theories that men had formed about the universe. What was accepted, and rarely questioned, in the sixteenth century may seem absurd when considered today. Yet without the insistent and radical teachings of a man like Galileo, there was no reason to doubt even the most archaic theories.

When Galileo burst upon the scientific scene, people still believed, for example, that the earth was the center of the universe and that the sun, the stars, and the planets moved in a circular course around it. Common sense told

17

them that if the sun rose in the morning and set at night-fall, it must be moving around the earth.

They believed too that the stars were made of some imperishable celestial fire. They were arrayed throughout the universe, which was itself a great sphere, smooth and transparent as glass, yet composed of elements sturdy enough to support all the heavenly bodies. That the stars and planets could be seen moving individually suggested that there must be a whole series of spheres arranged one inside the other with each supporting its own heavenly body.

Nothing in the heavens would ever fall down; every-thing moved without change. On earth, conversely, every-thing was perishable and in a constant state of change. The earth and the universe around it composed two oppos-ing and irreconcilable realms, according to sixteenth-century thought. Man's concept of earth and its relation to the heavens was based on ideas and theories of the Greek philosopher Aristotle, who died in 322 B.C. Aristotle, who had been a disciple of Plato's and a tutor to Alexander the Great, wrote profoundly on such varied subjects as logic, psychology, zoology, and literature.

It is not surprising that a man of Aristotle's intellect should apply his reasoning powers to the nature of the universe. He did so with beauty, logic, and wisdom— though without offering experimental proof for his ideas.

His writings on nature were one of the major legacies of the classical world. Fortunately they survived the col-lapse of the Greek empire, and, collected by the Alex-andrian scientist Ptolemy, they also endured the fall of Rome. Eventually they found their way into the Arab cul-ture and from there to the near and distant parts of the known world. Yet for all his philosophical wisdom and intellectual sharpness, Aristotle advanced a wholly in-correct conception of the physical sciences—astronomy in particular.

It was unfortunate that no one had the wit or the stature to challenge him before he became a kind of saint. In the Middle Ages his writings were taught without question in monasteries and also in Church schools and universities.

The illustration at left was made for the 1496 translation of Ptolemy's work, the Almagest. *The translator is shown on the right, Ptolemy on the left, of an armillary sphere, which, like the sextant used by the astrono-mer above, was an instrument for measuring the elevation of the sun.*

The theories he set forth became part of Christian dogma, and anyone who dared to challenge them was chastised for questioning God. Thus Aristotle's mistaken, unproved ideas of astronomy and physics were preserved; they were still being taught in Galileo's lifetime, nearly nineteen centuries after the great Greek philosopher's death.

During that long span of time the Church never wavered in its acceptance of Aristotelian law. And since all schools were Church controlled, Aristotelian theories continued to be accepted by scholars and taught throughout Europe. A few scientists had shown by experiment that the Greek philosopher's ideas on planetary motion were false. Some had even written books contradicting Aristotle. But until Galileo's lifetime, most of the men who argued against Aristotelian theories lacked what Galileo had in abun-

For a time, Galileo studied medicine, another branch of learning revived during the Renaissance. In the hospitals of his day occurred scenes such as the one in the fifteenth-century painting below—a patient with a leg wound is treated amidst general confusion. In the drawing at right, a doctor sets a patient's broken arm by using the classical method of applying a traction splint.

dance: the willingness to fight for the truth of his ideas.

As a challenge to Aristotle, or as a threat to any other great figure, the son of Vincenzio Galilei could hardly have appeared less impressive. Vincenzio himself had proved incapable of making anything prosper, and who would think his son could do better? Vincenzio, well-educated and a rather talented musician, had moved his family from his native Florence to Pisa, where, in vain pursuit of an adequate income, he had become a cloth merchant. There Galileo was born on February 15, 1564, and there the family grew to include three sons and four daughters. But by the time Galileo was a young man, the family had returned to Florence, no richer for the round trip.

Yet Vincenzio remained ambitious for young Galileo, who was his first-born son, hoping that the boy would become a painter or a musician. Indeed he fostered these hopes by instructing Galileo in music as well as in drawing. Reluctantly admitting that the family needed money-makers more than artists, he decided to train the boy as a wool merchant. It was a destiny with some promise, but Vincenzio had cause to regret his decision many times during his son's youth, for the boy developed exceptional musical and artistic skills.

Vincenzio finally did alter his plans for Galileo when the boy was nearly seventeen. He scraped together enough money to enroll Galileo in the University of Pisa as a medical student. The medical profession was considered honorable and also had the advantage of eventually producing an income.

But when Galileo reached the university and commenced his studies, he found himself more intrigued by the lectures on Aristotle's physics than by those dealing with medical science. He read the ancient texts of both Aristotle and Plato, and he also read texts that opposed Aristotle. These latter works were little known then and certainly were not favored by his professors—men who had memorized the writings of Aristotle and expected their students to do the same. Any discussion of the laws of nature ended when an apt quotation from Aristotle had been found. This was the method of both instruction and proof—hardly stimulating for debating ideas or expanding knowledge.

Galileo memorized the approved texts, just as he was directed. But dissatisfied with answers that seemed of doubtful validity, he reacted in an outspoken way, questioning Aristotle's statements. He expressed doubt, in fact,

At the University of Pisa, Galileo walked into the great lecture hall through this high portal. Affixed to the walls are dozens of student plaques.

22

that many of them were true at all. His behavior was unprecedented, and his consistently outspoken nature earned him a nickname used by professors and students alike. They called him the Wrangler.

He was neither surly nor unmanageable, but he clung to his beliefs. He was convinced that the true nature of the universe was yet to be seen; his teachers believed it had already become law.

Even during vacation periods, Galileo pursued his studies with diligence. In the sixteenth century some mathematical works of ancient philosophers had been translated and published; educated people were aware of the usefulness and the puzzles of geometry, algebra, and trigonometry. A story is told of a visit Galileo made to the palace of Francesco de' Medici, Grand Duke of Tuscany, in the winter of 1582–83. Inside the great palace, he happened to pass a room in which the Medici children were being taught mathematics, and he paused to listen. The children's tutor, Ostilio Ricci, was explaining a problem in geometry. Galileo suddenly became aware of the powerful logic of geometric proof, and according to legend, he hid behind the door, hoping to hear more. He was intensely interested in what was being taught but did not wish to admit his ignorance of it.

At last his desire to learn overcame his feeling of shame, and he asked the tutor to instruct him too. Ricci was delighted, and after a short period of supervised study, Galileo had grasped the principles of geometry so well that he could continue on his own. He studied every text he could find. By this time, the work of a long-forgotten Greek mathematician—Archimedes of Alexandria—had been discovered, translated, and printed. Archimedes had lived in the third century B.C., and his work had, for all intents and purposes, been buried with him. Now that it had been published, Galileo could study the great scholar's writings and absorb his ideas and techniques. Unlike Aristotle, Archimedes was in many ways a "modern" scientist, for he experimented to prove his theories. Since Galileo preferred working in just this way, he became a devoted reader of Archimedes' texts.

Archimedes had discovered the truth about several important natural laws, but more significant—at least from Galileo's standpoint—was Archimedes' discovery of a way to solve problems. He had discerned that a scientist must first separate what he truly wants to solve from irrelevant externals and then attack the core of the problem with boldness and imagination. Galileo realized that this approach was suitable for his own studies, though it differed from what he had been taught at the university. His professors, and most men of learning since the time of Aristotle, mixed questions of physics with questions of religion and philosophy. From reading Archimedes, Galileo came to see that the truth about nature could be unraveled best by first disregarding religion.

By the end of his third year at the University of Pisa, Galileo was as well trained as any scientist of his day. He had begun to be recognized for the brilliant young man he was, but he was constantly at odds with his teachers. Each new discovery he made gave further evidence that Aristotle's physics was incorrect—and so were the professors who taught it.

Galileo's father worked hard to supply his oldest son with money enough to remain in the university. But after three years Vincenzio reached the limit of his resources. In desperation he tried to obtain a scholarship for the young scientist. But because Galileo's scholastic record was poor—his answers to questions were rarely the "right" ones—none of his teachers would recommend him. They reasoned that free tuition should not be granted to anyone who believed that Aristotle's physics was wrong. Thus Galileo's formal education ended. He left the university, without a degree, in 1585.

But he continued his scientific studies when he went home to Florence. He was more determined than ever to become a mathematician and physicist. To the despair of his father, he did not seek employment; nor did he show any desire to settle down in some form of business. For the next four years he remained at his studies, probing into the scientific works of the ancient writers. He decided to become a mathematics professor, which distressed his family enormously. At that time a professor of mathematics earned the equivalent of sixty-five dollars a year. A professor of medicine, however, could earn well over two thousand. But Galileo had given up his medical studies.

During his years of study and experiment at the University of Pisa, he had made a strong impression on Guidobaldo del Monte, a nobleman who was also a gifted mathematician. Recalling this, he wrote to Guidobaldo to enlist the scientist's aid in obtaining a professorship. Through Guidobaldo's influence, Galileo came under consideration for the position of lecturer in mathematics at the University of Pisa. Though he was only twenty-five, and though his

Galileo traveled through the valleys and over the ridges of central Italy to reach Pisa where he was first a student and then a professor. This village nestled in the hills near Pisa has buildings that date back to medieval times.

student years at the university had not been particularly happy ones, Galileo was appointed to fill the position.

He left Florence and journeyed through the valley of the Arno with mixed feelings of hope and apprehension. He knew he was disliked at Pisa and that he would find life difficult there, but he was determined to continue his studies and also to have his say. He was ever "the Wrangler," and he returned to the university to the annoyance of nearly all of its faculty. During his three-year stay there, he would set into motion a new train of scientific thought that was to propel him through a brilliant, however tempestuous, career.

II

BODIES IN MOTION

From the time of his discovery of the principle of the pendulum, Galileo had been interested in the study of motion.
But until he joined the university faculty, he had neither
the time nor the facilities to work on the problem. As he
proceeded with his experimentation, he was guided by a
precept he had found in the writings of Archimedes. The
Greek scientist had warned his successors of the pitfalls
of asking too many questions about a problem at once.
Before Galileo had paid heed to this warning, men had
sought to know why as well as how things moved. Galileo
chose to ignore the *why* and concentrate on answering
the *how*. Thus the law of the simple pendulum is merely
a scientifically accurate description of an unexplained fact.

Similarly, one of his first experiments on motion was
essentially an attempt to show how bodies actually fall.
It was also a direct challenge to Aristotelian theory, for
the Greek philosopher had written: "A given weight moves
(falls) a given distance in a given time; a weight which
is as great and more moves the same distance in a less
time, the times being in inverse proportion to the weights."

According to this reasoning, a forty-pound boulder
would fall to earth from atop a sheer cliff two times faster
than a boulder weighing but twenty pounds and traveling
the same distance. By Galileo's time, some scientists knew
this theory was false; however, the writings of Aristotle
were still thought irrefutable, and no one dared question
their validity. Indeed, a number of experimenters had
dropped weights large and small from high walls and
church towers, but the results, which disproved Aristotle,
were not widely publicized.

*Before a window framing the leaning tower is a letter in which Galileo
wrote of his experiments. With it are two stone balls like those he is
said to have dropped from the tower, also seen in the view of Pisa above.*

Galileo was certain that Aristotle's reasoning was false. He refused to accept the logical-sounding proposition that two stones tied together would fall twice as fast as a single stone. Legend has it that to disprove this belief Galileo dropped stones from the top of the leaning tower of Pisa. Modern historians do not believe he actually used the tower, but he did succeed in proving that a one-pound sphere and a ten-pound sphere would strike the ground almost simultaneously when dropped from a high place.

Experimenting in public was not for Galileo, but persuasive writing was. Two of his best-known works, *Dialogue Concerning the Great World Systems* and *Discourses on Two New Sciences* were written in the vernacular to reach a wide audience. In the latter masterwork, the *Discourses*, Galileo expressed his theory of falling bodies by means of an imagined conversation between three characters: Simplicio, who believed in Aristotle's physics; Salviati, a spokesman for Galileo, and Sagredo, an intelligent layman who might be persuaded by whichever side was the more convincing. Here is an example of their argument:

Salviati: I greatly doubt that Aristotle ever tested by experiment whether it be true that two stones, one weighing ten times as much as the other, if allowed to fall at the same instant from the height of, say, 100 cubits [a cubit is about 18 inches] would so differ in speed that when the heavier had reached the ground, the other would not have fallen more than 10 cubits . . .

Sagredo: . . . I, who have the test, can assure you that a cannon ball weighing 100 or 200 pounds, or even more, will not reach the ground by as much as a span ahead of a musket ball weighing only half a pound . . .

Simplicio: Your discussion is really admirable; yet I do not find it easy to believe that a bird-shot falls as swiftly as a cannon ball.

Salviati: Why not say a grain of sand as rapidly as a grindstone? But, Simplicio, I trust you will not follow the example of many others who divert the discussion from its main intent and fasten upon some statement of mine that lacks a hair-breadth of the truth, and, under the hair, hide the fault of another that is as big as a ship's cable. Aristotle says that 'an iron ball of 100 pounds falling from a height of 100 cubits reaches the ground before a one-pound ball has fallen a single cubit.' I say that they arrive at the same time. You

Galileo dedicated his Dialogue *to Ferdinand II, Grand Duke of Tuscany, seen here as a cavalier.*

The three characters who debated a sun-centered universe and other concepts in Galileo's Dialogue *and* Discourses *are shown on the title page at right.*

DIALOGO
di
GALILEOGALILEILINCEO
AL SER.mo FERD. II. GRAN. DVCA DI
TOSCANA

Stefan Della Bella F.

29

ue ama
ui et equifi

falmon le f
fon liure

find, on making the experiment, that the larger outstrips the smaller by two fingerbreadths . . .; now you would not hide behind these two fingers the 99 cubits of Aristotle, nor would you mention my small error and at the same time pass over in silence his very large one.

Although the words spoken in the *Discourses* were invented by Galileo, each speaker bore some relation to a real person. Simplicio, spokesman for all the conventional ideas contained in the blind acceptance of Aristotle, may have been modeled after Lodovico delle Colombe, a Florentine scientist and philosopher who had sought to discredit Galileo. Much of what Simplicio says in the *Discourses* seems to have come from one of Colombe's dissertations.

Salviati, who echoed Galileo, was a reflection of Filippo Salviati, a close friend of the scientist's. Giovan Francesco Sagredo, who became one of Galileo's most respected advisers, was the third interlocutor—the open-minded one—in the *Discourses*.

In proving new theories, Galileo consistently anticipated questions that doubters and dissenters might put to him. His *Discourses* by its very nature contained both pros and cons. Galileo hoped he had reasoned his arguments carefully enough to convince the Aristotelians, who were the majority, that his ideas were correct.

Galileo believed, for example, that if it were possible to create a vacuum, any two falling objects would travel the same distance in the same time within the vacuum. He felt that in a completely airless space his proposition on free fall would prove exact, without even a "two-fingerbreadth" difference. Actually, even in an ideal situation, there would be some difference, but Galileo would never know this, for he did not know how to produce a vacuum. And Aristotle had taught that a vacuum was impossible to create.

Thus Galileo was forced to make allowances for air resistance in setting down his theories on free fall. And by this means he was eventually able to account for the varying speed of a falling body. Every scientist who had observed such an object felt certain that it gained speed the farther it fell. Galileo became the first to try to measure the acceleration of a falling object, and his success repre-

This fanciful mechanism, called the Clock of Wisdom, was designed by the illustrator of a fifteenth-century manuscript. Europeans had weight-driven clocks during the Renaissance, but none accurate enough to time experiments.

sented a break-through in solving the mysteries of natural law.

An object dropped to the ground from a point as high as a hundred-foot tower would hit the ground in but two and a half seconds; objects dropped from lesser heights would fall in fractions of seconds. Measuring these brief periods of time accurately down to an infinitesimal fraction of a second would be difficult even today; in Galileo's day it was impossible. Clocks were unreliable, and there was no way to measure seconds, let alone fractions of seconds. Galileo knew he would have to slow down the motion of falling bodies—to such a degree that their speed could

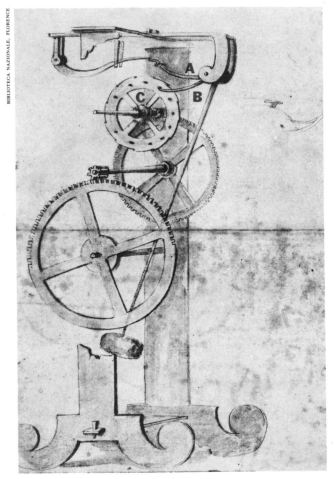

The most accurate timepieces of the Greeks and Romans were water clocks, like the one above at right: as the water level in the base rose, the cupid pointed to higher-numbered hours. Galileo invented the pendulum clock; his sketch above at left shows how each pendulum swing allowed a "finger" (A and B) to release one peg of the wheel (C) so that the wheel might turn.

be measured—without changing the essential character of the motion. But how was he to do this?

The answer came to him in his laboratory. It involved an inclined plane. Galileo discovered that by allowing a "falling" sphere to roll down a grooved strip of wood that was slightly inclined, he could slow down the sphere enough to study its motion. His knowledge of motion was such that he determined that while the eye would see only a ball rolling down a strip of wood, reason would discern that the ball was moving in two directions at once. As it was moving vertically down, it was also moving horizontally forward. The eye then was really seeing a combination of these two motions—the observable motion of a sphere rolling down a plane.

Galileo advanced the idea that the downward roll of a sphere along a plane was identical in nature to the motion of a dropped ball, except that the roll of the sphere was occurring more slowly. Experimenting further, he found that he could even control the slowness of the fall. If he adjusted the plane so that it was horizontal, the sphere did not move downward at all; he had slowed the falling motion to zero. If he inclined the plane slightly, the ball rolled slowly down the plane; therefore he had made it fall slowly. An increase in the slope of the plane increased the speed of fall. If Galileo increased the angle of incline to 90 degrees, the ball would fall rapidly, as though dropped.

Having devised this means for decreasing the motion of falling objects, Galileo had to determine how to measure, or at least compare, time intervals with some accuracy. He finally concluded that a modified version of the ancient Egyptian water clock would be effective. In describing the timing machine that he improvised, he wrote:

For the measurement of time, we employed a large vessel of water placed in an elevated position. To the bottom of this vessel was soldered a pipe of small diameter giving a thin jet of water, which we collected in a small cup during the time of each descent, whether for the whole length of the channel [inclined plane] or for a part of its length. The differences and ratios of these weights gave us the differences and ratios of the time intervals, and this with such accuracy that although the operation was repeated many times, there was no appreciable discrepancy in the results.

In his laboratory at Pisa, he and an assistant set up a grooved and polished inclined plane. They adjusted the water clock, and using a round ball of hard bronze, they began the long process of experiment and observation. As Galileo described it:

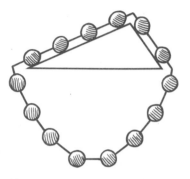

The inclined plane was a factor in experiments by other scientists of Galileo's day, including the Dutch mathematician Simon Stevin. An illustration for one of his works is this diagram—a frictionless chain stretched about a right triangle—which analyzed the physical forces acting on an inclined plane.

. . . we let the ball roll down the channel, noting . . . the time required for the descent. We repeated this experiment more than once to be sure of the time of descent . . . Having performed this operation until assured of its reliability, we now let the ball roll down only one quarter of the length of the channel, and having measured the time of its descent, we found it to be precisely one half of the former. Next we tried other distances, comparing the time for the whole length with that for the half, or for two thirds, or for three fourths, or indeed for any fraction. In such experiments, repeated a full hundred times, we always found that the distances traversed were to each other as the squares of the times.

This squared relationship was not explained or questioned in Galileo's report; he was merely stating how a ball "fell." His description of this process became further refined (but not further analyzed) in later years. He discovered that "the distances traversed, during equal intervals of time, by a body falling from rest, stand to one

At the center of this fresco stands Galileo, explaining to an enthralled audience the "falling" of a sphere down an inclined plane. The glum observer at far right is Giovanni de' Medici.

another in the same ratio as the odd numbers beginning with the unity [namely, the ratios evident in the series 1:3:5:7:9] . . ." A ball that falls one inch in one tenth of a second will fall three inches in the next tenth of a second and so forth.

With these experiments Galileo succeeded in unlocking the secret of uniformly accelerated motion. His theory was that the speed of an object increased the farther it fell, and, in addition, that the rate of increase was the same with each equal addition of distance. This was the phenomenon as Galileo described it: "A body is said to be uniformly accelerated when, starting from rest, it acquires equal increments of velocity during equal time intervals."

From discoveries like this came powerful mathematical principles that formed the foundation of the modern science of mechanics. With each step that Galileo took in his laboratory, one more precept of Aristotelian physics was proved false. And with each new disclosure, which

TRIBUNA DI GALILEO, MUSEO DI FISICA E STORIA NATURALE, FLORENCE

Galileo described in his lectures, the Aristotelian professors he worked with became angrier and more fearful. Friends cautioned him about the growing animosity of those who opposed him, but he paid little heed, preferring to continue with his experiments.

During the period in which he was studying the phenomena of motion, Galileo made other notable discoveries. One of these is still being pondered today by scientists examining the perils and possibilities of space travel. Galileo observed that a ball set rolling on a perfectly horizontal plane would come to rest only because of friction from surfaces in contact with it and, of course, because of the retarding effect of the air. What would happen, he asked himself, if all retarding forces, including friction, were removed? He concluded that once a ball was in motion, it would roll on forever in a straight path—out beyond the earth and through infinite space, on and on.

The ultimate ramifications of his answer were inconceivable even to him, for he did not know that all the retarding forces on earth could be removed. Moreover, it did not occur to him that the theory he had formulated—which is now called the principle of inertia—had practical application to astronomy and the study of planetary movement. Nor could he have foreseen that his principle would someday permit man to hurl satellites deep into space.

Galileo's boldness in challenging accepted ideas earned him renown while he was at the University of Pisa, but not among his fellow professors. The men who taught traditional physics rejected his radical ideas without ever coming to grips with them. But the class of intellectuals produced by the Renaissance, that period in which classical learning and culture were revived, grasped Galileo's new knowledge eagerly. As his fame grew and spread, Galileo was called on more and more frequently to solve physical problems. One day Grand Duke Ferdinand I of Tuscany asked him to inspect a model of a dredging machine and render an opinion on how well the finished apparatus would work. Galileo consented to do so.

Unhappily, the machine had been designed by Giovanni de' Medici, who in addition to being the governor of Leghorn province was also the Grand Duke's half-brother. He was a man of considerable power and influence, and he considered himself something of a genius. However, when Galileo examined the model, he announced in his usual emphatic way that it could not possibly work.

This pronouncement pleased no one. The machine was

completed according to Giovanni's original design. When it was put to dredging the harbor of the city of Leghorn, it proved a failure, just as Galileo had predicted. However, instead of enhancing Galileo's reputation, the machine's malfunction served to pave the way for his downfall. Giovanni de' Medici and the professors at the university became allied in a conspiracy the intent of which was to force Galileo out of the teaching profession. Soon he was hissed at whenever he entered his lecture hall, and so many other petty annoyances were thrust in his way that his daily life became intolerable.

Realizing the futility of trying to maintain his position, Galileo finally decided to resign. This action removed the insults that had been directed against him, but it thrust on him new pressures that were no less demeaning. He was as poor and insecure now as he had been as a student. An additional liability was the fact that his father had died, and Galileo, as the eldest son, was responsible for the livelihood of his entire family.

Back in Florence, the twenty-seven-year-old scientist was forced to borrow money to provide a dowry for one of his sisters. And then he had to help one of his brothers

TEXT CONTINUED ON PAGE 40

The Medici were powerful in Tuscany for two centuries and helped spread the Renaissance throughout Italy. Ferdinand II, to whom Galileo dedicated his Dialogue, *was a grandson of Ferdinand I (below), a splendid and capable ruler. One of his brothers, Giovanni (below, left), was a sometime inventor and considered himself Galileo's rival.*

37

Padua, where Galileo was granted a professorship in 1592, had different customs than Pisa. This painting of

birited religious procession in Padua, with monks and professors on parade, was made in the sixteenth century.

The face of Italy was scarred by both natural and artificial barriers in Galileo's day. His route from Florence to Padua took him across the Apennines and Tuscany's border into the wealthy republic of Venice.

TEXT CONTINUED FROM PAGE 37

find employment. His own uncertain future was what troubled him most, however, and he was forced to turn to his friends. Eventually, through their assistance he received an appointment to the chair of mathematics at the University of Padua. A year had passed since he had left Pisa. It was 1592, and Galileo was so poor by then that he walked from Florence to Padua, a distance of more than a hundred miles, carrying his belongings on his back.

At Padua, Galileo entered what was probably the happiest phase of his life. His salary was generous enough for him to live comfortably and at the same time help his family. Even more important, however, was the fact that he received the courtesy and respect of his colleagues. Galileo never ceased working. In the summers, when other teachers happily embarked on holidays, he returned to Florence to tutor Grand Duke Ferdinand's young son, Cosimo, in mathematics. Galileo wished to restore himself to the good graces of the ruling Medici family, for he hoped to return to Tuscany eventually and in a position of some importance.

During the next eighteen years, Galileo's work was productive and varied. He wrote at length on each new mathematical principle he uncovered. His treatises were consistently revealing and frequently more than a little prophetic. For example, to conclude his dissertation on accelerated motion, he wrote:

The theorems set forth in this brief discussion, if they come into the hands of other investigators, will continually lead to wonderful new knowledge. It is conceivable that in such a manner a worthy treatment may be gradually extended to all the realms of nature.

His own part in the expansion to "all the realms of nature" he could not then foresee. But far away in the Low Countries a new scientific instrument was being invented. Aided by this device, a telescope, Galileo was destined to see further than any man before him.

The University of Padua, whose colonnaded courtyard is seen in the cutaway drawing below, was one of the major centers of Renaissance learning; it was founded in 1222.

A NEW VISION

Galileo was not the first man of vision to question the truth of the Aristotelian universe. As early as the third century B.C. there was someone who doubted. He was Aristarchus, from the Greek island of Samos, and he strongly believed that the earth rotated on its own axis and that the sun lay at the center of the universe.

Seventeen hundred years later a Polish churchman and astronomer developed his own sun-centered theory of the universe. He was born Niklas Koppernigk, but he soon adopted the Latinized form of his surname: Copernicus. It was his belief that the sun was the center of the universe and that the earth and the planets revolved around it. This concept, set down in a massive volume, is known and still respected as the Copernican theory. Copernicus died twenty-one years before Galileo was born.

Although Copernicus differed with Aristotle on the structure of the heavens, he shared the Greek philosopher's belief that the moon and the planets revolved in absolutely perfect circular paths. The mixture of religion and science that Galileo helped to separate is rarely better illustrated than in this particular error. Aristotle had believed that the sun and all the planets moved about the earth in perfect circles because, as he wrote, "All that is eternal is circular." To Aristotle, the circle signified perfection: it had neither a beginning nor an end and was without flaw. Surely the gods would not allow an imperfection in heaven; therefore the planets must move in circles. By the same reasoning, celestial spheres, on which the stars rested, must also spin in perfect circles.

The logic seemed sound enough, but repeated observations tended to disprove it. Over the centuries astronomers were becoming aware that the planets moved erratically in their circular paths about the earth. To account for this, it was determined that the planets must be moving not only in circular fashion about the earth but must be twirl-

The gentleman in the flowing gown is the rector of the University of Padua. This caricature was made about the time of Galileo's residence there.

ing in other, smaller circles as well. These other circles, called epicycles, relate to the larger circles as small wheels rolling on the rims of larger wheels.

Scientific and religious thought were so intermingled that even the most radical thinkers believed planets moved in a circular fashion. But one man did not: a Danish astronomer named Tycho Brahe.

In 1577 Brahe glimpsed a comet streaking across the sky. He had been a firm believer in Aristotle's theories, but as he observed the course of the comet, he became convinced that solid, transparent spheres did not exist to carry each star and planet—else the blazing comet would have shattered them. He realized then that the idea of an earth-centered universe was wrong, but he would not accept Copernicus' theory. Instead he developed a theory that was a combination of both concepts. Brahe agreed with Aristotle and Ptolemy that the earth was the focus of the universe. But he insisted that all the planets revolved about the sun as it moved around the earth.

After Brahe's death, one of his former assistants, Johannes Kepler, embarked on a massive study of his teacher's notations and writings. Kepler's work took place at about the same time that Galileo began making his own astronomical observations. Unlike Brahe, Kepler was a Copernican, but in testing his master's theories as well as some notions of his own, he reached conclusions that modified and improved the Copernican idea of a solar system. Kepler discovered that planetary motion about the sun was not circular, as even Copernicus had thought, but elliptical—with the sun at one focus of the ellipse.

Kepler and Galileo shared similar viewpoints, and though one lived in Germany and the other in Italy, it was inevitable that they should correspond. And through the exchange of letters they became good friends. In 1609, Kepler sent a copy of *New Astronomy*, his book about planetary motion, to Galileo in Padua. In response, Galileo acknowledged both the book and the brilliance of its author in a letter that said in part:

I count myself happy, in the search after truth, to have so great an ally as yourself, and one who is so great a friend of the truth

TEXT CONTINUED ON PAGE 49

Galileo refrained from teaching the revolutionary theory of Copernicus that the sun was at the center of the universe. Copernicus' original manuscript is at right, posed in the Polish university where he studied. The circular orbits diagramed on the open page are reproduced more clearly above.

44

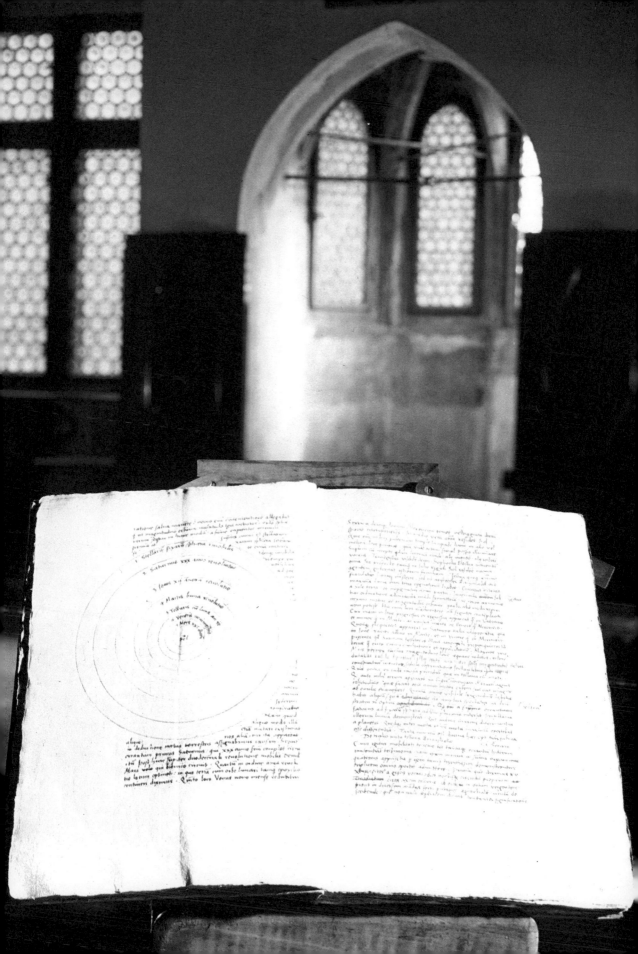

KEYS TO UNLOCK THE UNIVERSE

Two milestones in Western science were the completion, around 1530, of Nicolaus Copernicus' great astronomical volume and the development of Galileo's telescope in 1609. In the same period three only slightly less important figures were working, all of whom struggled with old concepts and odd instruments. They were Peter Apian (1501–52), Tycho Brahe (1546–1601), and Johannes Kepler (1571–1630). Apian, a German known for his contributions to mathematics and geography, invented the torquetum, the large device shown on the opposite page. It could be adjusted to measure the altitude of celestial bodies above the horizon; with it Apian was also able to resolve spherical triangles and trace the course of comets. Above it, on a snake-entwined stand, is a quadrant used by the Danish astronomer Tycho Brahe. On this page, above, is shown the frontispiece of the astronomical book that Kepler published in Germany in 1619. The illustration depicts an imaginary observatory held up by several decrepit columns (representing the ancient scientists) and two new pillars (Copernicus and Brahe). As the sign hanging from the roof of the pavilion indicates, Kepler dedicated his book and its astronomical tables ("Tabulae Astronomicae") to the Holy Roman Emperor Rudolf II, who gave to science in Central Europe the same patronage the Medici granted it in Italy. Some rulers of the day hoped that court astronomers would stake out claims for them in the heavens; but people of all nations benefited equally when Galileo and his contemporaries began to unlock the secrets of the universe.

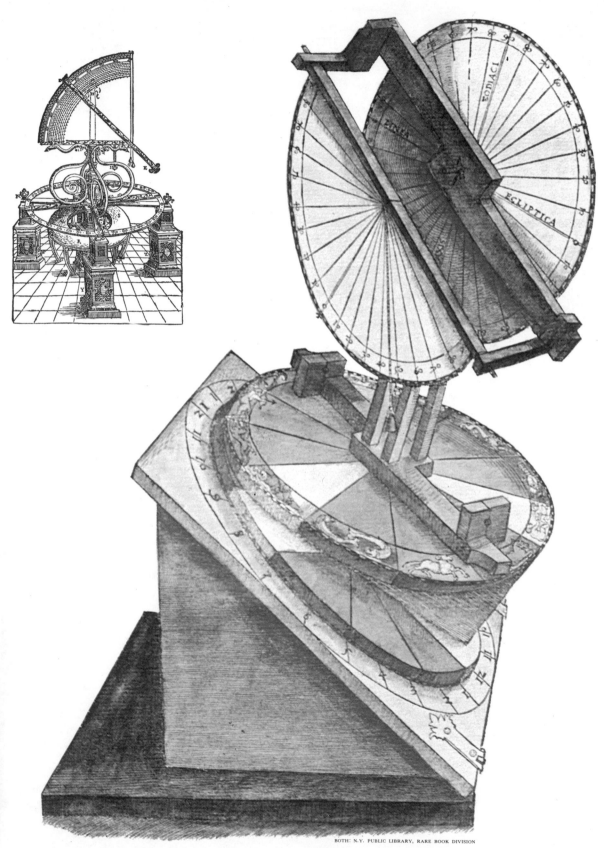

47

EFFIGIES TYCHONIS BRAHE O. F.
ÆDIFICII ET INSTRVMENTORVM
ASTRONOMICORVM STRVCTORIS
A° DOMINI 1587 ÆTATIS SVÆ 40

TEXT CONTINUED FROM PAGE 44

itself. . . . I shall read your book to the end, confident of finding much that is excellent in it. I shall do so with the more pleasure because I have been for many years an adherent of the Copernican system, and it explains to me the causes of many of the appearances of nature which are quite unintelligible on the commonly accepted hypothesis [Aristotle's idea of the earth as the center of the universe]. I have collected many arguments for the purpose of refuting the latter, but I do not venture to bring them to the light of publicity for fear of sharing the fate of our master Copernicus, who, although he has earned immortal fame with some, yet with very many (so great is the number of fools) has become an object of ridicule and scorn . . .

Kepler, more certain than ever that Aristotelian errors should be exposed, urged Galileo to publicize his views on the Copernican theory. But as Galileo lacked proof to support his views, he rejected the suggestion. He knew well the intellectual blindness of his Aristotelian colleagues at the university, and he could not help being aware that if he tried to upset the very heavens, the Church of Rome would react vigorously and mercilessly against him. If he ever doubted this, he had only to recall the recent fate of suspected heretics who were pursued, tried, and condemned by the Inquisition. That all-powerful tribunal of the Roman Church was set up to deal with people whose beliefs were thought to be contrary to the Church. One such heretic, the philosopher Giordano Bruno, had been a rebel just like Galileo—and had dared to spread the theories of Copernicus as well as other suspect ideas. After a lengthy imprisonment, he had finally been burned at the stake. With Bruno as an example and a reminder, Galileo knew he would have to be cautious.

It was early summer, 1609, the year Kepler's great book reached him, that Galileo first learned of the invention of a new and extraordinary optical device. By using it, so people said, one could bring distant objects nearer the eye. Without ever seeing the device, which was the first telescope, Galileo deduced its principles and succeeded in building one of his own. In retrospect, it can be seen that when Galileo completed his first telescope, the ancient world of Aristotle and Ptolemy began a gradual but ceaseless disintegration. Of this powerful invention, Galileo wrote to his brother-in-law on August 29, 1609:

Tycho Brahe, at left in his observatory on the island of Hven, points to a wall slot through which an assistant (center, right) sights a quadrant. Above is a sketch of Kepler, the astronomer who utilized Brahe's findings.

Before Galileo's day, many philosophers believed that good luck and bad were controlled by the stars; they used astrological tables like the one painted at left to determine the relationships between the heavenly bodies. Galileo devised the first astronomical telescope in 1609 to help man view the skies scientifically. Two of these are shown on the ornate stand at right.

. . . I have a piece of news for you, though whether you will be glad or sorry to hear it I cannot say, for I have now no hope of returning to my own country [Tuscany], though the occurrence which has destroyed that hope has had results both useful and honorable. You must know that about two months ago a report was spread here that in Flanders a spyglass had been presented to Prince Maurice, so ingeniously constructed that it made the most distant objects appear quite near, so that a man could be seen quite plainly at a distance of two miles. The result seemed to me so extraordinary that it set me to thinking, and as it appeared to me that it depended upon the laws of perspective, I reflected on the manner of constructing it and was at length so entirely successful that I made a spyglass which far surpasses the report of the Flanders one. As the news had reached Venice that I had made such an instrument, I was summoned before their Highnesses, the Signori, and exhibited it to them, to the astonishment of the whole Senate. Many of the nobles and senators, although of a great age, mounted more than once to the top of the highest church tower in Venice in order to see sails and shipping that were so far off that it was two hours before

they were seen, without my spyglass, steering full-sail into the harbor; for the effect of my instrument is such that it makes an object fifty miles off appear as large as if it were only five . . .

The sadness to which Galileo refers at the beginning of his letter was a direct result of his having built a telescope. So astonished were members of the Venetian Senate and the faculty of the University of Padua that they immediately made sure that a lifelong professorship was conferred on Galileo. While this appointment solved his financial worries—his salary was to be a most generous one—it kept him from returning to Florence, where he longed to live.

Once the question of his future had been disposed of, and once Galileo had resigned himself to it, he turned to making improvements on his telescope. By the time he had completed the fifth such instrument, "sparing neither labor nor expense," as he put it, Galileo had an instrument that made objects appear thirty times nearer and a thousand times larger.

Although many experimenters all over Europe were

St. Mark's Square in Venice, seen in the 1649 engraving below, was one of the most brilliant settings of the Italian Renaissance. From nearby Padua, Galileo was called to Venice, where he demonstrated his telescope from the top of the bell tower (in background, at left).

PIAZZA DE S. MARCO DI VENETIA.

soon grinding lenses, no one managed to develop an instrument as powerful as Galileo's. And Galileo did not cease making improvements on his telescope until he had turned out more than a hundred. The sensation his telescope created would be difficult to imagine today. Poets sang its praises, and crowds gathered whenever a man appeared on the streets carrying one of Galileo's curious and remarkable instruments. For Galileo the highest possible recognition was given to him when he took a brief trip home to Florence. There he demonstrated his telescope to Cosimo II, whom he had tutored as a boy and who was now Grand Duke of Tuscany. Reportedly, the Grand Duke was quite impressed.

The telescope was regarded as more than a novelty. Galileo himself had pointed out to prominent Venetians how well it could spot approaching fleets and observe enemy troop movements from the safety of a distant hill. But Galileo also perceived that by turning the telescope skyward much could be learned of a universe which, until then, had existed mainly in men's minds. Aristotle's idea of the heavens involved an array of perfectly smooth spheres: sun, moon, and planets. Doubting this concept, and eager to know the truth, Galileo chose the nearest of so-called flawless spheres—the moon—as the first object of his telescopic scrutiny.

He observed it night after night, noting its changing phases. One of the first things to become apparent to him was the contours of the moon. Studying the sphere shortly after a new moon, he realized that the line separating the overwhelming dark region from the thin crescent of brightness was not a uniform curve; instead the line was rough and uneven, indicating the inclines and declivities of mountains and valleys. With some accuracy Galileo was able to estimate the height of the mountains on the moon by observing the shadows they cast and by measuring the changing angle of the sun's rays. Further, he surmised correctly that the faint light delineating the dark portion of the moon when only thin portions are visible is sunlight reflected from the earth. Today this phenomenon is called earth shine.

Not all of Galileo's observations were correct, however. His telescopes were still relatively crude instruments, and his interpretation of what he saw was based primarily on common sense. He assumed, for example, that the dark areas on the face of the lighted moon were seas. In reality they are vast plains or deserts that appear dark whenever

Atop the bell tower, noblemen of Venice throng to examine two of Galileo's instruments (background). The scientist (standing at right) explains a star chart to Venice's ruler.

tall mountains blot out the sun's slanted rays and thus create deep shadows. Galileo's misconception can perhaps be forgiven, but it will never be forgotten; the dark areas are still referred to as seas.

In sum, Galileo's lunar observations served to disprove the Aristotelian thesis that heavenly bodies were perfectly spherical objects. And by proving that the moon had a rough-textured surface similar to the earth's, he nullified the theory that the earth and the rest of the universe belonged to two distinct realms.

Galileo's astronomical discoveries went far beyond his surveillance of the moon. Sweeping the night sky with his telescope, he noted the presence of many more stars than anyone before him had seen. The mysterious Milky Way, which stretched like a misty veil between the horizons, had engaged the wonder of astronomers for centuries. Galileo's examination of it, late in 1609, revealed that it was not a mist but a vast and distant belt of numberless stars. And then on January 7, 1610, he focused his telescope on the planet Jupiter.

His first long look showed him what seemed at first to be three small, bright stars near the planet. Two lay to the east of Jupiter and one to the west. He noticed too that they lay in a straight line, as though on an axis that passed through the planet itself. For Galileo that night marked the beginning of what would be a long series of observations of these curious new objects. He noted their positions—two to the east, one to the west—and then looked at them again on January 8. The bright objects were still visible, but they had changed positions. Now they all lay in a neat row on the west side of Jupiter. Galileo was incredulous, for according to all previous observation, stars held unchanging relationships.

Galileo could hardly wait until darkness came the next night, but he was destined for disappointment. The weather had become overcast, and clouds obscured the heavens; he had to wait another day. On January 10, to his surprise, he saw only two stars, and both were on the east side of Jupiter. It was then that Galileo began to doubt that the bright objects were really stars. He pondered their motions, and the movement of Jupiter. The stars always appeared in a line; only their locations changed. At first he concluded

Sidereus Nuncius, GALILEO, 1653

In the upper drawing, the eastern half of the moon's surface reflects light; this is called a first-quarter moon. Below it, the western half of the same surface reflects light, making a third-quarter moon.

The painting at left by Donato Creti shows two young Italians examining the moon's surface by means of a telescope similar to those made by Galileo.

Entries in Galileo's notebook record his sightings of Jupiter and the several satellites that appeared with it in various combinations.

that the changes were due to Jupiter's motion, but he decided at last that contrary to everything then known, the stars themselves must be moving.

On January 11 he saw two stars again, both to the east of the planet; one appeared much brighter than the other. The next night, three stars were visible; two were on the east, and one was on the west side of the planet. On January 13, a fourth star became visible. Two nights later all four stars lay to the west of Jupiter, all approximately in a line.

At first Galileo was certain that a new group of moving stars had been found. Then it became clear to him that he had been observing four satellite bodies whirling about Jupiter. They were not stars, or even planets, but moons. With this conclusion came the total collapse of the Ptolemaic theory, at least as far as Galileo was concerned. For it seemed logical that if these moons could revolve about Jupiter, then obviously all heavenly bodies did not revolve about the earth. The whole concept of the solar system would have to be revised—even the Copernican theory. Copernicus had been able to see that the moon revolved about the earth, but since the earth went around the sun, so, according to his logic, did the moon. Galileo, clarifying the point, was to write:

It is now not simply the case of one body revolving around the earth, while the two together make a revolution around the sun, as the Copernican doctrine teaches us; but we have the case of four bodies, or moons, revolving around the planet Jupiter, as the moon does around the earth, while they all with Jupiter perform a grand revolution around the sun in a dozen years.

Galileo named the four moons after four members of the Medici family: the brothers Cosimo II, Francesco, Carlo, and Lorenzo. News of Galileo's discovery soon swept across Europe, arousing storms of furious debate. The French court, envious of the fact that immortality was being given the Medici, urged Galileo to search the heavens assiduously for another new star. If he found one, they asked that he call it the Grand Star of France.

Galileo continued his exploration of the sky but found nothing more for a while. Then in midsummer of 1610, he began a scrutiny of Saturn. His interpretation of what he saw was incorrect, but his surveillance led to the eventual discovery of what is known today as Saturn's ring. Describing what he believed he saw, Galileo wrote:

I have observed with great admiration that Saturn is not a single star but three together, which, as it were, touch each other . . .

the middle being much larger than the lateral ones . . . by employing a glass which multiplies the superficies [visible boundaries] more than a thousand times, the three globes will be seen very distinctly and almost touching, with only a small dark space between them.

He sent this information immediately to a friend in Florence but swore the friend to secrecy. Galileo wanted more time to observe his discovery before announcing it publicly. However, he feared that some other possessor of a telescope might encounter the same phenomenon before he had completed his work; thus it was important that an associate be entrusted with a document attesting to Galileo's prior claim on the discovery. He took further precautions by sending a bewilderingly coded message to other friends in Italy, and also in Germany. They puzzled long over it but were unable to unscramble SMAISMRMIL MEPOETALEUMIBUNENUGTTAVIRAS.

By November, 1610, Galileo felt free to divulge what he had seen. Decoded into intelligible Latin, his message read, *Altissimum Planetam Tergeminum Observavi* ("I have observed that the farthest planet is three-mooned").

This discovery dealt another setback to Ptolemy and to the other exponents of Aristotle. The ancients had believed that the heavens were eternal, unchanging, and incorruptible—and further that nothing new could be discovered in the skies. This belief could no longer be taken seriously, for within the course of one year, Galileo had found four moons around Jupiter and had discovered a hint of the cosmic disturbance that surrounds Saturn. And there were more discoveries to come.

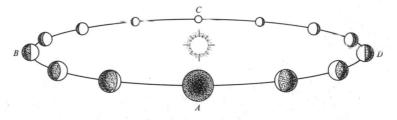

The upper two drawings of Saturn at left show the planet as Galileo observed its changes through his relatively low-power telescope: Saturn looks like a jug with detachable handles. In fact, Saturn is surrounded by three very extensive but thin rings of ice particles (bottom drawing). Above is a sketch of Venus' phases as Galileo finally explained them: the planet circles the sun from A to D and reflects the most light at C; but it seems no brighter at C than at B because it is then farther away from the earth.

Dark and indistinct islands seem to float on the sun's surface in this lumi-
nous painting of sunspots made at the Hayden Planetarium in New York.

Turning his attention to Venus, Galileo perceived that it underwent changes of phase just as the moon does. Sometimes Venus appeared to be a crescent; at other times it appeared a whole sphere. He had noted that the phases of the moon were caused by the variable illumination of the moon's surface—sometimes the earth blocked the sun's rays, and men could see only a small portion of light reflected from the moon, and sometimes all the moon's surface served as a reflecting disc. The phases of Venus, he reasoned, must be a similar phenomenon. Thus, Venus must revolve about the sun, which was the source of the light that Venus reflected.

Predictably the doubters insisted that if Venus really did revolve around the sun, it should appear larger when it was near the earth and small when it was far away. Instead, it seemed not to alter its size at all.

Galileo explained that when Venus is nearest the earth, only a small portion of its surface reflects sunlight visible on earth. Thus it resembles a new moon. When Venus is farthest from the earth, it lies on the far side of the sun, and sunlight reflected from the entire surface is visible from the earth. It then resembles a full moon. More light reflected from a greater distance makes Venus seem the same size as when it is near the earth but reflecting only a little light. Without a telescope to aid the eye, Galileo concluded, Venus would appear constant in size and brilliance.

Galileo destroyed still another traditional belief through his telescopic observations of Venus. For that planet was believed to be a luminous body made visible by its own, self-generated light—like the sun. According to Galileo, Venus was illuminated by the sun's rays. He was on the brink of realizing that all the planets were nonluminous bodies made visible by light reflected from the sun.

He looked now to the other planets—to Mercury and Mars—but intense study of these celestial bodies revealed nothing of significance at the time. There was only one object left, the only one that could be studied through his relatively low-power telescope. That object, which held the key to the structure of the universe, was the sun. By shielding his telescope with a piece of dark glass, Galileo was able to direct it toward that great boiling star, and as the months passed, he made daily observations. It was an exhausting procedure, and Galileo recognized it as a climactic struggle—the final assault on man's traditional concept of the universe around him.

Near the end of 1610, Galileo's solar inspection brought

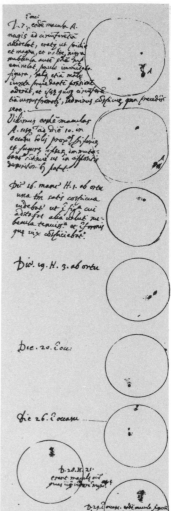

Sidereus Nuncius, GALILEO, 1610

The jottings above in Galileo's handwriting describe the course of sunspots across the sun's face—and perhaps behind it. They were the basis for his 1613 Letters on the Solar Spots in which he mentioned the rotation of the sun.

results. By that time he had been observing a number of dark spots on the sun's surface. At first he assumed they were small bodies momentarily located between the earth and the sun. But as the days passed, the dark spots appeared to change their shape, sometimes drifting together and sometimes moving apart. Also, they moved across the face of the sun in a straight line, and when they reached the rim of the sun, disappeared.

By continuing his observations for several months, Galileo experienced the satisfaction of seeing the dark spots reappear from the opposite side of the solar disk. Now it was clear: the sun rotated on its axis—the same motion that both Galileo and Copernicus believed the earth followed. Thus, Galileo's discovery of sunspots had far-reaching significance.

Despite all his new evidence to support the Copernican theory, Galileo was torn between caution and boldness. He did not lecture on his revolutionary findings before students at the University of Padua. Instead he continued to teach the Ptolemaic system. And when he published any of his findings, he did not directly attack the reigning theories. Even so, his published material brought angry outcries from many traditionalists. Of his discovery of the moons of Jupiter, the famous Jesuit mathematician Clavius of Rome said sneeringly, "Let Galileo keep his opinions and welcome. I hold to mine."

Two professors, one at Padua and one at Pisa, flatly rejected Galileo's conclusion. The Pisan, Julius Libri, died late in 1610, still refusing to look through a telescope. Galileo commented caustically that as Libri, in life, had disbelieved the existence of Jupiter's moons, he might now believe in them as he passed by en route to heaven. One learned Aristotelian wrote and published his disgust with Galileo, saying:

We are not to believe that nature has given Jupiter four satellites in order to immortalize the name of the Medici. These are the dreams of idle men who love ludicrous ideas better then our laborious maintenance of the heavens. Nature abhors such horrible chaos, and to the truly wise such vanity is detestable.

What raised the hackles of these stubborn traditionalists was not the certainty that Galileo's ideas were wrong, but concern that he might be right. The Aristotelians' rising fear fairly leaps from the page of a pamphlet that was published in Venice in 1611 and written by one Francesco Sizi of Florence. It says in part:

*Galileo's table was piled with books and instruments. He was also inter-
ested in magnetism; he astonished visitors by such experiments as lifting
a heavy model of a coffin (on the stand in background) with a small magnet.*

61

... these satellites of Jupiter are invisible to the naked eye, and therefore can exercise no influence on the earth, and therefore would be useless, and therefore do not exist. Besides, the Jews and other ancient nations, as well as modern Europeans, have adopted the division of the week into seven days and have named them after the seven planets. Now if we increase the number of planets, this whole and beautiful system falls to the ground.

Thus religious and scientific thought had become so entangled that mere opinions became absolute, and any new ideas seemed opposed to accepted beliefs. Men cried out in protest and in rage, which caused Galileo to write to Kepler, his friend and supporter:

What is to be done? . . . I think, my Kepler, we will laugh at the extraordinary stupidity of the multitude. What do you say of the leading philosophers here to whom I have offered a thousand times of my own accord to show my studies, but who, with the lazy obstinacy of a serpent who has eaten his fill, have never consented to look at the planets, or moon, or telescope? Verily, just as serpents close their ears, so do men close their eyes to the light of truth.

In his long period of service at the University of Padua, Galileo brought honor, as well as controversy, to the institution. He had accepted a lifetime professorship and appeared to be settled. But he yearned for his homeland, Tuscany, and for Florence, his family's native city. He also wished to be freed from the chores of lecturing and tutoring so he could write of his discoveries. As early as May, 1610, he had addressed a letter to the Tuscan secretary of state in which he declared that his ultimate wish was "to have sufficient leisure to enable me, before my life comes to a close, to conclude three great works which I have in hand." Grand Duke Cosimo II, who had respected Galileo since childhood, responded by expressing his eagerness to have the renowned scientist affiliated with his court. Cosimo believed that Tuscany offered a better climate for Galileo's scientific pursuits than the republic of Venice, where Padua lay. In this the Grand Duke was only partly correct.

Venice, unlike Tuscany, was a true republic. The Venetian Senate, its ruling body, was sharply opposed to any foreign intervention, even if cloaked in the sacred authority of the Church of Rome.

But Tuscany was not so free. The grand dukes, its rulers, remained subservient in fundamental matters to the Church of Rome. Galileo, at the point of beginning his first great scientific treatise, made the crucial mistake of

In 1623 Galileo published a book on comets and other heavenly phenomena called The Assayer *("Il Saggiatore"—title page above). While not heretical, or even outspoken about Copernican theories, the book demonstrated Galileo's conviction that the real universe was the one that could be observed.*

leaving what protection he had in Venice and placing himself in jeopardy in Tuscany.

In the summer of 1610, Galileo was named first mathematician at the University of Pisa and philosopher and mathematician to the Tuscan court at Florence. He was forty-six years old when he returned to Tuscany, certain that the most difficult years of his life lay behind him. Now, he hoped, life would be placid and he would have the opportunity to write his books and enjoy the rewards gained from his achievements. He hoped too that he would be able now to express his theories to his students.

These were naïve hopes for someone who had upset traditional conceptions of the nature of the universe. As he had bluntly jarred men's beliefs, he could not escape the necessity of answering for his actions. Not long after Galileo returned to Florence, he felt the effect of his enemies' first concerted effort to bring him down.

New stars were discovered and familiar ones examined by Galileo's improved telescopes. This drawing from his 1610 treatise, The Starry Messenger, *shows Orion's Belt (three large stars across the top) and Orion's Sword (the five large stars grouped toward the bottom).*

296

IV

THE CRIME OF GALILEO

Galileo's early experiments on the motion of falling bodies had disproved Aristotle; his later astronomical discoveries were interpreted as casting doubt on the Bible. Angry churchmen pointed to the contradiction between Galileo's belief that the earth moved about the sun and the biblical assertion that Joshua had commanded the sun to stand still. Stubbornly, these dogmatists argued that if the sun was fixed at the center of the universe—as Copernicus and Galileo insisted—then how could Joshua have observed the sun to be moving? Their interpretation of the Bible was literal and unyielding.

In Pisa and in Florence, the rumor spread that Galileo was a heretic who questioned biblical truth. The sarcasm with which he replied to his critics did nothing to win new allies, and the ranks of his enemies grew. Soon university officials at Pisa ordered that no theory or discovery of Galileo's was ever to be mentioned or taught—to which Galileo responded once again contemptuously. He declared that the ignorance of his enemies had been the best master he had ever had, since their blindness had forced him to make many experiments to demonstrate the validity of his discoveries.

Galileo was waging a fight over the right of a scientist to teach and defend his beliefs. Thus, even though he recognized the undercurrent rising against him, he refused to suppress his discoveries or temper his statements. He had proof, he insisted, that Aristotle's concept of a changeless heaven was false. Further, he said he felt no compunctions about modifying or revising outmoded theories. Nature, he said, "in order to aid our understanding of her great works, has given us two thousand more years of ob-

When Galileo was in Rome to meet with Church officials in 1624, Ottavio Leoni did this crayon portrait of the embattled sixty-year-old scientist.

servations, and sight twenty times as acute as that which she gave Aristotle." This explanation, despite its logic, would not satisfy his enemies, and Galileo knew it. He was always aware that his work would provoke criticism, even condemnation. In a letter to a friend, following an important discovery, Galileo expressed certainty that the Aristotelians would immediately "put forth some grand effort to maintain the immutability of the heavens."

Just what this "grand effort" would be, Galileo did not of course know. He received a hint of it early in 1613, after a friend of his, a monk named Benedetto Castelli, had dined with members of the Tuscan court. Mealtime conversation that evening had focused on Galileo's discovery of the moons of Jupiter. One of the guests, a distinguished professor of physics, told the Grand Duchess Christina that while Galileo's discoveries might be true, the conclusion drawn from them that the earth moved about the sun was contrary to the Bible.

To Castelli, who overheard the scholar's remark, hiding behind biblical authority to denounce a scientific theory seemed contrary to the rules of academic fair play. The monk felt obliged to defend Galileo. Apparently he made a strong impression on the Grand Duchess, who was alarmed at the widening breach between science and religion.

After the dinner, Castelli wrote immediately to Galileo to inform him of the evening's discussion. Both men knew that if university professors were to convince the Church that Galileo's beliefs were heretical, his career would be ruined.

Until this incident, Galileo did not allow his religious faith and his study of science to interfere with each other. Though a devout Catholic, he was able to separate the two spheres of his life. To him each step out of the darkness of ignorance into the light of truth was further cause for belief in divine creation and control. But after Castelli's warning, Galileo recognized the need to set forth his views on the relationship between science and religion. On December 13, 1613, he wrote to Castelli saying:

. . . I think it would be the better part of wisdom not to allow anyone to apply passages of Scripture in such a way as to force them to support, as true, conclusions concerning nature the contrary of which may afterward be revealed by the evidence of our senses or by necessary demonstration. Who will set bounds to man's understanding? Who can assure us that everything that can be known in the world is known already?

Castelli allowed the letter to circulate. When its con-

Grand Duchess Christina was the powerful regent of Tuscany during the youth of her grandson Ferdinand.

66

tents became known there was a noticeable easing of tensions. Soon, even the Grand Duchess Christina's doubts had been removed. For all the surface calmness, however, the seeds of opposition were finding fertile soil deep within the Church. And nowhere was the opposition so actively at work as in Florence.

The first overt clerical attack took place in December, 1614. Standing in the pulpit of the Dominican Church of Santa Maria Novella in Florence, Father Thomas Caccini delivered a sermon that denounced mathematics as inconsistent with the Bible and detrimental to the State. And then, to drive home his venomed attack, the angry monk declaimed this biblical passage:

Then spake Joshua to the Lord in the day when the Lord delivered up the Amorites before the children of Israel, and he said in the sight of Israel, Sun, stand thou still upon Gibeon. . . . So the sun stood still in the midst of heaven . . .

Always the skillful speaker, Galileo discourses with a skeptical cleric. He is pointing toward the sun, which he believed was at the center of the earth's orbit and, according to him, only seemed to rise and set because of the revolutions of the earth on its own axis. On the table at his left is an armillary sphere; this model appears to represent the Ptolemaic universe, which puts the earth in the center.

Word of Caccini's sermon, which was an indirect censure of Galileo, spread quickly through Florence. Many people were shocked, and Galileo's friends grew fearful and uneasy. It had begun to seem that Galileo's beliefs really did contradict the Bible. Not so, said the scientist, and then explained his reasoning:

... I do not think it necessary to believe that the same God who gave us our senses, our speech, our intellect, would have us put aside the use of these, to teach us instead such things as with their help we could find out for ourselves, particularly in the case of these sciences, of which there is not the smallest mention in the Scriptures ...

Many intelligent churchmen sided with Galileo, and a high dignitary in the Dominican order, Father Maraffi, even apologized to Galileo for Caccini's outburst. But the damage had been done, and Florence was in an uproar. In Rome, however, many of the strictest clerics seemed unconcerned—and were still reading Galileo's works with interest. A number believed, in fact, that his writings were destined to be recognized as established truths.

Then Father Caccini unleashed the ultimate weapon. He went to Rome and asked to be received in secret by the Inquisition. He told the tribunal that Galileo was a scoffer at saints and miracles, even at God Himself. He declared that Galileo corresponded not only with suspected heretics but actually with German Protestants—an obvious slur against Kepler. Caccini was a master at mixing innuendo with derision, and in the judges of the Inquisition he had a ready audience. When he had finished attesting to the godlessness of Galileo, the Inquisitors were aroused. It was not long before another rumor was being whispered among Florentines—to the effect that an undercover investigation of Galileo had begun.

So vigorous was the reaction in Florence that Galileo decided to go to Rome to explain his position and outline his beliefs to the heads of the Church. It would not have been in character for him either to capitulate to the pressures placed on him or to compromise. In June, 1615, six months before leaving for Rome, Galileo expanded the explanatory letter he had written to Castelli and sent it as a formal memorandum to the Grand Duchess Christina.

In this paper he set down his position as a scientist and as a true Catholic. He tried to emphasize that the Holy Spirit intended that the Bible should teach man how to go to heaven, not how the heavens go. He hoped that such an argument, when passed on to Rome, would help his cause.

As biblical armies clash, Joshua commands the sun to stand still.

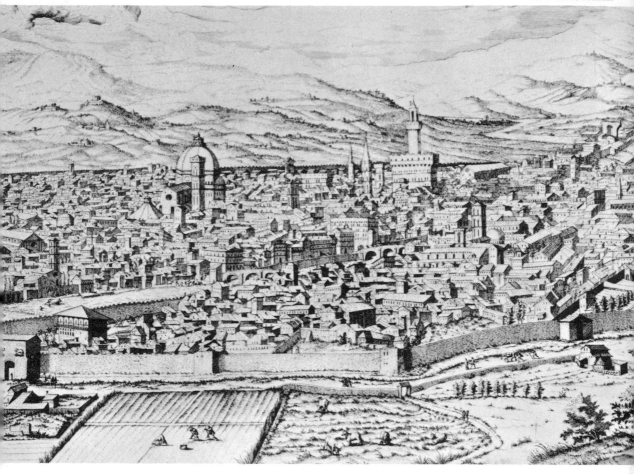

Life and death in Tuscany were regulated from offices in the two prominent buildings in this view of Florence: the high-domed cathedral and the spired town hall.

A Roman prelate, Robert Cardinal Bellarmine, who served as a member of the Holy Office (the Inquisition), summed up the view of the Church in the matter of how the heavens went in this extract from a letter written to a Carmelite monk Paolo Antonio Foscarini:

. . . the words 'The sun also ariseth, and the sun goeth down, and hasteth to his place where he arose' were written by Solomon, who not only spoke by divine inspiration, but was a man wise above all others and learned in the human sciences and in the knowledge of all created things, which wisdom he had from God . . .

Implied strongly in the text of this statement was Bellarmine's assertion that anyone who believed the theories of Copernicus was questioning the wisdom of Solomon and hence the Bible. Galileo was obviously in this category.

Although Bellarmine had been present when Galileo had been denounced by Caccini, the Cardinal's evalu-

The climax of Galileo's long struggle with the Church was his recantation, of which a transcript appears above, dated June, 1633. Also displayed here is the title page of the Dialogue, which at first received Church authorization.

ation of Galileo's argument was not reported to the Inquisition. Bellarmine knew that the scientist was being investigated, but at this point he did not press for a ruling against him. Nor was he particularly eager to have Galileo come to Rome to answer his critics. Probably Bellarmine knew that the Inquisition did not yet have a solid case against Galileo. He must also have realized that despite frequent illnesses, Galileo was a persuasive and dynamic man whose presence in Rome might score heavily against Church opposition.

But in December, 1615, Galileo did go to Rome, and soon his efforts to win clerical approval seemed to be meeting success. Even Caccini, the man who had maligned him, was told to apologize. Galileo's eloquence won him many admirers. As one witness to his forceful debating wrote to a certain Cardinal d'Este in Florence:

Your Reverence would be delighted with Galileo if you heard him holding forth, as he often does, in the midst of fifteen or twenty, all violently attacking him, sometimes in one house and sometimes in another. But he is armed after such fashion that he laughs all of them to scorn . . .

Certainly Galileo was well armed against verbal attack, but against the forces that were already conniving against him, there was no defense. At last he was summoned to appear before Cardinal Bellarmine. To Galileo's surprise the Cardinal told him that the Copernican theory had been determined to be "in error." Therefore, Bellarmine advised, Galileo should abandon the idea that the sun was the center around which the earth and the other planets revolved.

The meeting apparently took place in February, 1616, although the only official record of it is a note in the Inquisition files. The note, which was unsigned and lacked a notary's seal, states that after the Cardinal had spoken, the Commissary General of the Inquisition stepped forward, and Galileo was "commanded and enjoined, in the name of His Holiness the Pope and the whole Congregation of the Holy Office, to relinquish altogether the said opinion . . . nor further to hold, teach, or defend it in any way whatsoever, verbally or in writing; otherwise proceedings would be taken against him by the Holy Office; which injunction the said Galileo acquiesced in and promised to obey."

This injunction by the Commissary General has been a source of unending puzzlement to historians. There is no evidence that Galileo "acquiesced" to anything—or that

TEXT CONTINUED ON PAGE 74

OVERLEAF: *As mathematician to the grand dukes of Tuscany, Galileo received some slight protection from the Inquisition. Seen here are the furnishings of the room near Florence where he worked upon his return from Rome; his tripod and telescope are standing by the window.*

PHOTO BY ERICH LESSING, MAGNUM

TEXT CONTINUED FROM PAGE 71

Above is a portrait of Benedetto Castelli, the scientifically minded monk who presented Galileo's case at the court of Tuscany. In 1629 Castelli became mathematician to Urban VIII (below), an equivocal pope whose initial support of Galileo later turned to hostility.

he knew he was forbidden to "hold, teach, or defend" what he felt certain was true. Some historians suggest that key phrases of the injunction may have been added later, which would explain why the document did not appear to have been authenticated.

Galileo's subsequent actions raise doubt that he ever realized the seriousness of his situation. He never imagined that he was liable to immediate arrest if he ever showed "in any way whatsoever" his Copernican leanings. Even so, he left Bellarmine's palace shaken and somewhat depressed. He had lost the battle to convince his Church that truth—even scientific truth—need not be considered contrary to belief in God.

By this time his problems were no longer theoretical, but actual. Rome was blackened by rumors that Galileo had at last been brought down, that he had been forced to recant. Hearing this whispered gossip, Galileo requested a statement from Cardinal Bellarmine describing what had occurred at their meeting. The Cardinal responded willingly. He certified that Galileo had not been forced to recant or to do penance for his erroneous beliefs but had been advised that the Copernican theory was contrary to the Bible and therefore was not to be held or defended. Apparently Bellarmine was unaware of the intervention of the Commissary General—or perhaps pretended to be.

Armed with the Cardinal's certificate, Galileo hoped once more to suppress his enemies, and for a time it appeared that he had done so. He lingered four more months in Rome, and before his departure he was received by Pope Paul V. The Pope, and many high churchmen, bore Galileo no ill will. How could they? for many had not read his books thoroughly nor thought out his logical and upsetting conclusions. Despite the pardon from the Church, Galileo still feared persecution. He expressed this concern in an audience with Paul V and was assured that neither the Pope nor the Holy Office would give heed to rumors spread against him.

Outwardly, at any rate, it seemed that Galileo had triumphed once again. Despite the rap administered by the Inquisition, the Church appeared to have forgiven him—and to have granted him permission to continue on his way as long as he said nothing that would collide with accepted doctrines. Though this may seem a suffocating kind of freedom, Galileo was comforted by it. It offered a way for him to avert persecution, and it gave him the impetus to make plans to go home. A Roman churchman

wrote the Grand Duke of Tuscany that Galileo would leave
Rome with "the best reputation" and that none believed
the rumors of his enemies. Yet another witness to Galileo's
activities in Rome, the Tuscan ambassador, did not feel
so positive of the scientist's future. He wrote also to the
Grand Duke, saying: "Galileo seems disposed to take on
the monks and to contend with personages whom you
cannot attack without ruin to yourself. It may any moment
be heard in Florence that he has stumbled into some bad
precipices . . ." His friends in Florence became alarmed.
The secretary of state to the Grand Duke wrote to Galileo,
hoping to speed his return:

You have had enough of monkish persecutions and ought to
know by this time what the flavor of them is. His Highness [the
Grand Duke] fears that your longer stay in Rome may involve
you in fresh difficulties and would therefore be glad if . . . you
would not tease the sleeping dog any more and would return here
as soon as possible. There are rumors flying about which we do
not like, and the monks are all powerful . . .

Coming from a trusted friend, this counsel would have
constituted words of caution, but as written by the Grand
Duke's deputy, it was an order. On June 30, 1616, Galileo
left Rome. He carried with him the signed statement of
Cardinal Bellarmine, but the germ of his eventual downfall lay in that unsigned note buried in the Inquisition files.

Galileo had not directed his energies solely toward
debate during the time he was in Rome. His questing mind
had grappled with an increasing number of scientific
problems. He had rarely been at rest. A problem solved
always led to another one awaiting solution. Ideas passed
through his inquiring mind to which he had to give voice.
He wrote of the tides, and he devised a means for deter-
mining longitude. But his health suffered—it had never
been very good—and finally broke down. For years following his return to Florence he was bedridden. Still he continued to work and write, and to correspond. But he lived
in virtual retirement at the villa of Bellosguardo near
Florence, and from there, for eight years, he maintained
an almost unbroken silence.

In 1621 Pope Paul V died. The next pope, Gregory XV,
lived only two years. Then to Galileo's delight, Maffeo
Cardinal Barberini, a friend and admirer, was elected
to the papacy, choosing the name Urban VIII. Galileo was
determined now to go back to Rome. He would press for
the withdrawal of the 1616 prohibition against his publicly
championing the Copernican theory.

TEXT CONTINUED ON PAGE 78

*When Galileo journeyed to Rome
in 1615, Paul V (above) was pope.
During his reign the Copernican
theory was declared heretical by
the Inquisition. The rather kindly
portrait (below) of the severe inquisitor Robert Cardinal Bellarmine is by an anonymous painter.*

Recoiling as if physically threatened, Galileo is pictured defending himself at his appearance before the Inquisit

Rome. Before him stands the presiding cardinal; at the long table in the background are the judges of the tribunal.

TEXT CONTINUED FROM PAGE 75

In planning a return to his former battleground, Galileo disregarded the advice of his longtime friend Giovan Francesco Sagredo, whose name Galileo eventually used in his *Dialogue*. Urging him to be content with what he already had, Sagredo wrote: "Philosophize comfortably in your bed, and leave the stars alone. Let fools be fools, let the ignorant plume themselves on their ignorance. Why should you court martyrdom for the sake of winning from their folly?"

For Galileo, no less of a wrangler than before, felt compelled to fight. In 1624, he traveled to Rome to talk with the Pope. To his dismay he found that as a cardinal Barberini had been able to hold private views favorable to Galileo and his scientific endeavors, but as pope he must steer a different course. Urban VIII welcomed his old friend from Florence, feted him, assured him of his warmest regard, and even conferred a pension on the learned scientist. But he would not withdraw the admonition. Instead he suggested that Galileo put his literary skills at the service of the authorities and enumerate all the pros and cons relative to new scientific theories. One stipulation was that Galileo should conclude his dissertation by stressing that the problem had not been solved, that God might have solved it by means beyond human consideration, and that Galileo must not constrain divine omnipotence within the limits of his theories. The Pope even dictated this conclusion for the proposed work, but Galileo would not agree to undertake the project.

For years Galileo had dreamed of giving the Copernican theory to the world, of explaining it so persuasively that no one could fail to see its truth. He had been admonished by the Church to which he remained loyal and, in spiritual matters, subservient. But he could not stop searching for a way to satisfy both his love of scientific truth and his love for his Church.

Finally, a way had become apparent. During the years of his semiretirement in Florence, he had worked on a book called *The Assayer*. It dealt with the nature of comets but was in reality a reply to attacks made on his physical discoveries. His views in it were erroneous, for he believed that comets, like rainbows, were atmospheric peculiarities that reflected sunlight. However, the significance of *The Assayer*, as far as Galileo's immediate future was concerned, was in its skillful writing rather than in its science. For the book managed to discomfit his enemies without violating Church doctrine; and though it stung the opposition, the book re-

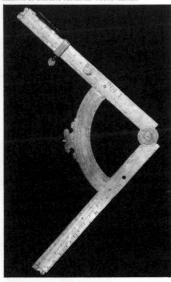

One of Galileo's inventions was this improved military compass; in making computations, it served the same purpose as a modern slide rule.

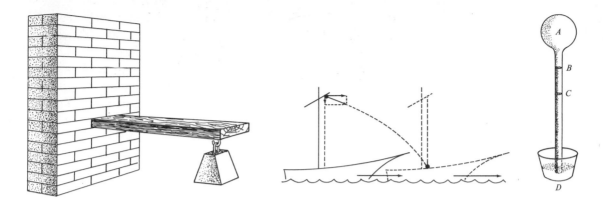

ceived the applause of the Pope himself, who had been cool to Galileo's pursuit of scientific discovery.

Galileo's method, which proved a most successful tactic, was to present his own theories simply as plausible ideas without stressing his firm belief that they were true. And as he deftly skirted the question of Copernicanism, he could not be accused of lending support to theories that were in conflict with the dogma of the Church.

The Assayer was printed in Rome in October, 1623, and its success had been one of the reasons Galileo had ventured to Rome to plead before the new pope. Its success also encouraged Galileo to turn to a long-cherished project, *Dialogue Concerning the Great World Systems*, after his return from Rome. He was sixty when he began it, and for five years thereafter, despite recurrent illness, he poured his best reasoning and most skillful writing into the volume. It is the book that introduces the three characters Salviati (champion of Galilean physics), Simplicio (an Aristotelian dogmatist), and Sagredo, the object of their persuasive speeches.

Galileo finished the manuscript at the end of 1629. By that time several changes had taken place in the Church that made Galileo hope he could obtain speedy permission to publish. His old friend Benedetto Castelli had been made mathematician to the Pope. Another friend, Niccolo Riccardi, had been named chief censor to the Vatican and would pass on the submitted manuscript. In addition, word had reached Galileo of Pope Urban's statement that if he had been pope in 1616, the prohibition against Galileo would not have been made. Had the Pope changed his mind? Galileo could not suppress his optimism.

With great expectations Galileo set out once more for

Rome. Castelli, Riccardi, and Pope Urban each received him warmly. His manuscript was read, and after minor alterations had been made, it was returned to him with the censor's general approval. Galileo had also written a preface and an epilogue designed to forestall all possible criticism and even incorporating conclusions dictated by the Pope. But at this point Riccardi began to realize that the text might not be so harmless as he had imagined and that by allowing it to be published he was becoming a kind of accomplice.

Galileo was allowed to return to Florence with the text, but the chief censor withheld the preface and the conclusion, thus preventing the book's publication. With the exercise of some pressure by Galileo, and with the help of the Tuscan ambassador to Rome, Galileo was given permission to submit the text to ecclesiastical censors in Florence and to have it approved there. With further prodding from the Tuscan ambassador, Galileo managed to retrieve the preface and the conclusion from Rome. So at last, after more than a year's delay, the book was published in February, 1632.

With its circulation throughout Europe, a virtual thunder of applause reached the old scientist. Congratulations poured in from every important center of learning—from kings as well as scientists, and from laymen who had read the book and had seen for the first time the truth contained in Galileo's new science. But the applause was not

Galileo had a lively, if somewhat sarcastic style of writing, which greatly appealed to those unskilled in scientific matters. At left is one of the several surviving copies of Galileo's vigorous signature.

unanimous. One of Galileo's most embittered enemies, Father Christopher Scheiner, a Jesuit astronomer from Ingolstadt, Germany, wrote in protest to an influential friend, "In these dialogues the author has made null all my mathematical researches . . . I am preparing to defend myself and the truth." But his preparations were, for a time, kept secret.

In Rome, Father Riccardi read the *Dialogue* and could not contain his growing uneasiness. Reportedly he said, "The Jesuits will persecute this with the utmost bitterness."

Father Riccardi prophesied correctly. For though the *Dialogue* appeared an impartial and noncommittal discussion, it presented an inescapable argument for the Copernican system and thus dealt a death blow to traditional theory. Father Scheiner and his colleagues succeeded in proving to the censors that they had been duped. The censors were persuaded that by allowing the *Dialogue* to be published, they had inadvertently allowed irreparable damage to be inflicted on the established system of teaching and on the authorities who backed it.

Shortly after its publication, orders came from Rome to stop printing the book. And in another order, the printer was commanded to remit to the Vatican all copies of the book remaining in stock. The printer wrote that he could not comply with the order as his stock was completely sold out.

Friends of Galileo pleaded with Pope Urban to intercede, but they were quickly informed that the Pope had grown furious with the scientist. Urban had come to believe that the Simplicio of the *Dialogue*, the Aristotelian, was a caricature of himself. Angrily he described Galileo as a man "who did not fear to make game of me." The scientist's friends did not doubt that the papal wrath would find an outlet.

On September 23, 1632, a message from Rome arrived at the residence of the Florentine Inquisitor. It directed him to "inform Galileo in the name of the Holy Office that he is to appear as soon as possible in the course of the month of October, at Rome, before the Commissary General of the Holy Office . . ."

Remembering all too clearly the fate of other men at the hands of the Inquisition, Galileo delayed as long as possible. Doctors attested to his advancing age and poor health. Friends and officials sought in vain to have the order withdrawn. In despair Galileo wrote to Francesco Cardinal Barberini, who was Urban's nephew:

Also an accomplished artist, Galileo drew this handsome compass on which north is seen at the right.

This vexes me so much that it makes me curse the time devoted to these studies in which I strove and hoped to deviate somewhat from the beaten path generally pursued by learned men. I not only repent having given the world a portion of my writings, but feel inclined to suppress those still in hand, and to give them all to the flames . . .

But all protestations failed. On January 20, 1633, the ailing scientist wearily set out to face the Inquisition. Once in Rome he waited several months for the tribunal to request his appearance. During this time he was kept in close confinement and interrogated now and then, but he was not mistreated. Surely there was no basis for either punishment or torture; despite the conviction of the Jesuits and other clerics that Galileo was a heretic, proof for this conclusion was not forthcoming.

His *Dialogue* had received the censor's approval; all the requested corrections had been made; the book had been granted the seal of approval required for the publication of any book in a Catholic country. Thus there seemed to be no basis upon which to substantiate charges against him. But one day someone riffling through the Inquisition files discovered the unsigned note setting forth the injustice of 1616. In it was the statement that Galileo had agreed no longer to "hold, teach, or defend it [the Copernican theory] in any way whatsoever, verbally or in writing . . ."

Galileo was sure that the words "in any way whatsoever, verbally or in writing" had not appeared in the original admonition of Cardinal Bellarmine or in the prelate's later explanatory note. He was certain too that though he had agreed not to hold or defend the controversial theory—which the *Dialogue* gracefully avoided—he had not been asked to refrain from teaching it.

Had his memory failed him? Was this an error, a forgery? Galileo would never know, for with these words as evidence, the Inquisition now had the means to deliver the final blow against him. On June 21, 1633, Galileo was convicted of disregarding the prohibition of 1616. The following day he knelt before his inquisitors and read slowly in a halting voice from a prepared apology:

I, Galileo . . . kneeling before you, most Eminent and Reverend Lord Cardinals Inquisitors-General against heretical depravity

At the center of this shrine in Florence stands a statue of Galileo. Above it are scenes from his life, two of which are shown on this page: the young scientist gazes at the lamp; the old master lectures his disciples.

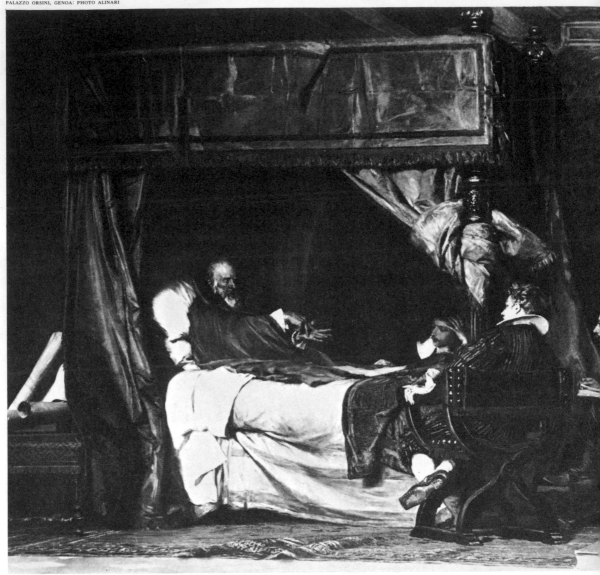

throughout the whole Christian Republic, having before my eyes
and touching with my hands the Holy Gospels, swear that I have
always believed, do believe, and by God's help will in the future
believe, all that is held, preached, and taught by the Holy
Catholic and Apostolic Church. But whereas—after an injunction had been judicially intimated to me by the Holy Office to
the effect that I must altogether abandon the false opinion that
the sun is the center of the world and immovable, and that the
earth is not the center of the world, and moves, and that I must
not hold, defend, or teach in any way whatsoever, verbally or in
writing, the said false doctrine . . .

His voice droned on and on as he enumerated the sins

In his bedroom at Arcetri, where he lived his last days, Galileo makes a point as his son (on the bed) and students listen eagerly.

he had committed and of which the tribunal had found him guilty. Upon completing his recantation—the true purpose of the trial—Galileo was not imprisoned, as many people believe. He was allowed to return to Florence and remained there under house arrest. His movements were restricted, and he was continually watched. The father of modern science had been humbled at last by his enemies—but not wholly subdued.

He was bedridden much of the time now, felled by bouts with asthma and painful ruptures, but he still fought back. In 1638, he completed the *Discourses*, a work which paved the way for those who later developed the science of mechanics. Not only did the treatise deal with theories of motion in falling bodies, but it discussed light waves, combustion, and the vibration of instruments to produce musical sound. The volume was printed in Protestant Holland, safely outside the jurisdiction of the Church of Rome. The *Discourses* was dictated to the Duke of Noailles, a French nobleman whose major virtue, from Galileo's point of view, was his distance from the Italian disputes which had so vexed Galileo.

Shortly before the *Discourses* was completed, inflammations in both eyes had caused Galileo to become blind. Nearly helpless now, he was cared for by his daughter and his friends; even the Grand Duke came to cheer him with conversation and a bottle of his favorite wine. But his spirit and intellect did not fail, and so he was able to continue his work almost to his last days by dictating his thoughts and theories to two of his loyal disciples. Finally a slow fever overcame him. In 1642, when he was nearly seventy-eight, he died. Still the Roman Church would not relax its judgment, and Galileo was buried in an unmarked grave.

His adherents mourned his death, certain that his years of work and wrangling had perished with him, that accepted Aristotelian and Ptolemaic doctrines would continue to be taught and believed. They could not have foreseen that the year Galileo died in Italy, Isaac Newton would be born in England. Whereas Galileo had discovered how things moved, Newton would discover why. And in so doing, he would advance Galileo's theories and refine them to the point of ultimate acceptance.

As Newton gained recognition for his discoveries, he would in effect be building a permanent monument to research and scientific discovery—and of course to his great predecessor, Galileo.

V

NEWTON AT CAMBRIDGE

Nothing outstanding in the background or in the childhood of Isaac Newton foreshadowed his later greatness. His parents were undistinguished countryfolk who lived on a small farm in Woolsthorpe, near Grantham, England, and earned a modest living from the land they tilled. Isaac's father died some months before the future scientist was born; on Christmas Day, 1642, friends came in to assist the young widow in childbirth.

Isaac Newton was born prematurely and underdeveloped. Legend has it that he was so puny he had to wear a supporting device around his neck to hold his head upright. In later years Newton took delight in retelling his mother's favorite story of his infancy—that he was so small she could have put him in a quart mug.

As he remained small during his boyhood, he was unable to join in the rougher games enjoyed by average-size boys his age. But he seemed not to miss the companionship of his fellows. He rather liked playing alone. He read a great deal; he devised games that could be played without partners or opponents; he also developed unusual skill in building mechanical toys. He did not experience the joys of family life as a child. When his mother remarried and went to live with his stepfather, Newton was sent to board with his grandmother. He attended the nearby day schools and later entered King's School in Grantham. There, more or less left on his own, he boarded with a family that lived in town.

Newton shared the manual dexterity and the fondness for invention that were characteristic of Galileo, but other-

Isaac Newton lived for much of his life at Trinity College, Cambridge University. His rooms were at right of the Great Gate, on the second floor.

wise the two men were strikingly dissimilar. Whereas Galileo was a hot-blooded jouster with a zest for life, Newton was a soft-spoken recluse who preferred to keep silent about his mighty secrets rather than fight in defense of them. Even when he became recognized as a scientist, the results of his experiments had to be pried out of him, and it could never be ascertained just exactly when his discoveries had taken place.

Despite his efforts, however, Newton did not always succeed in avoiding conflict. Ironically, it was as a result of a fight he had while enrolled in the Grantham school that he began making strides as a student. Newton's nephew, John Conduitt, recalled the incident later from Newton's own description of it:

When he [Newton] was last in the lowermost class but one, the boy next above him, as they were going to school, gave him a kick in his belly which put him to a great deal of pain. When school was over, Newton challenged him to a fight, and they went into the churchyard. While they were fighting, the Master's son came out and encouraged them by clapping one on the back and winking at the other. Isaac Newton had the more spirit and resolution and beat him [the bully] till he would fight no more. Young Stokes [the Master's son] told Newton to treat him like a coward and rub his nose against the wall, and accordingly Newton pulled him along by the ears and thrust his face against the side of the church. Determined to beat him also at his books, by hard work he finally succeeded and then gradually rose to be first in the school.

But having reached the top, Newton stopped working almost immediately and turned to the thing he most enjoyed—building intricate mechanical toys. Among these efforts was a windmill he mounted on the roof of the house he boarded in and a water clock that remained in that house for many years and worked as well as the best clocks of the day.

He regarded these activities as serious enterprises, though others did not. For diversion he chose to build and fly kites. He found extra amusement in attaching a candle lantern to one of his kites and flying it at night. The sight of a swaying light flickering in the dark sky was guaranteed to alarm the Grantham townspeople. They were certain the light was a comet, which in those days was viewed as an inexplicable—and frightening—supernatural occurrence.

Newton set aside his toys and contraptions only when his top-ranking status in school was threatened. This casual attitude irritated his teachers, but even his head-

Woolsthorpe, Newton's birthplace in Lincolnshire, England, is depicted above in a drawing made by his lifelong friend Thomas Stukeley.

master had to admit that a young man for whom education was so effortless must be inordinately bright.

After four years at King's School, Newton returned to Woolsthorpe. His stepfather had died, and his mother, who had come back to the farm, wanted Newton to take on duties as head of the household. He was sixteen now, old enough to assume responsibility for the management of the farm. But he proved to have no aptitude for it. He dawdled and daydreamed. He allowed the animals to stray. Nor did he express interest in any other kind of career. Certainly he had neither the competitive inclination of a businessman nor the physical vigor to become a soldier.

It was a difficult time for a mother to try to make plans for the future of her bright son. All across Europe political unrest was stirring, and in England itself the first of two crippling civil wars had begun the year Newton was born. A soldier named Oliver Cromwell had led a Puritan rebellion against King Charles I, and in 1649, after the king had been beheaded, the English Commonwealth was established. Cromwell eventually became its Lord Protector, and he reigned virtually as a dictator until his death in 1658. As Newton's teenage years ended, the royal line

The engraving below shows Trinity College as it looked when Newton studied and taught there. The garden that supplied his food is left of the Great Gate (foreground). In 1954 a cutting from the famous apple tree at Woolsthorpe was planted in this garden as a memorial.

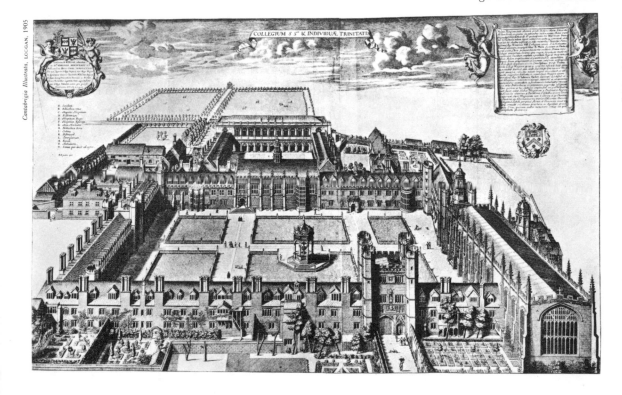

COLLEGIUM S S^e & INDIVIDUÆ TRINITATIS

Cantabrigia Illustrata, LOGGAN, 1905

was restored, and Charles II put on the English crown. The tumult was over, but even so, opposing religious factions maintained an underlying state of strife.

Eager for her son to find some activity that might serve him well in these times, Newton's mother let him return to school and prepare for Cambridge University. When he finally entered Trinity College, Cambridge, he had completed his preparatory work, but he had demonstrated no greater zeal for scholarship. His lack of enthusiasm for academic work is quite understandable: in 1661, when Newton entered Cambridge, the kind of in-

"Take away this bauble!" demands Oliver Cromwell, referring to the mace of the Speaker of the House of Commons. Cromwell, the Puritan general who ruled as England's dictator during Newton's boyhood, became impatient with Parliament and its recalcitrant members when they hesitated to do his bidding.

struction that had frustrated Galileo in Italy years before still prevailed in England. The imaginative theories of Copernicus and Kepler continued to be ignored, and Galileo's work remained unrecognized. Most people still believed that the sun revolved about the earth.

But the reluctance of institutions in England and on the Continent to accept new scientific theories had produced one good effect—a number of scientific societies had been founded that functioned freely outside the halls of traditional learning. The societies were formed by professors and amateur scientists who desired an exchange of ideas among themselves and men of similar aptitude and curiosity at home and abroad. First thought of as "invisible colleges," the societies soon became internationally known as clearing houses for new discoveries and inventions. In France, for example, there was the Paris Academy of Sciences. In England there was the Royal Society, formally known as the Royal Society of London for Improving Natural Knowledge. It was founded officially in 1660, one year before Newton entered Cambridge; however, its members had met periodically and had been in correspondence with one another for some years prior. The Royal Society was to provide the stimulus for most of England's future exploration and scientific discovery. Newton would come to regard it first as a welcome platform for his theories and then as an impenetrable wall of resistance.

At Cambridge, Newton was aloof and uncommunicative much of the time: possibly he was very homesick. He was a country boy for whom the usual pattern of student life—the horseplay and the political debates and the whirl of social activities—was alien and unwelcome. Newton once fled from his room, through a hail of jeering laughter, while his roommate was entertaining boisterously. At every opportunity he went home to Woolsthorpe. As time passed, his silence became more complete, his reserve more pronounced.

During his three years at Cambridge, Newton followed the customarily prescribed course of study, which included the mathematics of the day: algebra, geometry, and trigonometry. He also took Latin and Greek, and under his tutor, Dr. Isaac Barrow, studied physics and optics—the science of light. Many scientists before him had been fascinated with the contradictory nature of light, some believing that it flowed like a liquid and others that it behaved like vapor; it was not long before Newton had read nearly everything written on the subject. So thorough did his

Among Newton's notebook jottings is a large item indicating that he received the sum of thirty pounds from his mother to pay for his Cambridge degree in 1667. Below is a sketch of his tutor, Isaac Barrow.

1	2	3	4	5	6	7	8	9	10	11	12	13	14	15
0.48	1.36	2.24	3.12	4.0	4.48	5.36	6.24	7.12	8.0	8.48	9.36	10.24	11.12	12.0
16	17	18	19	20	21	22	23	24	25	26	27	28	29	30

On this handsome, complex dial at Queen's College, Cambridge, well-briefed students can read the time (by sunlight or moonlight), the day, and the month, as well as the proper zodiacal sign. It is called Newton's Dial, even though it was probably installed after his death.

mastery of optics become that Dr. Barrow asked Newton to read and comment on a paper that the professor himself had written.

Dr. Barrow was a scholar of considerable eminence who had been called to Cambridge to hold an honored position, the Lucasian chair of mathematics. He was first to recognize the genius in Newton and, indeed, was responsible for its application. For when Dr. Barrow introduced Newton to telescopes and to the existing and conflicting theories of light, Newton's giant intellect suddenly awoke.

He studied telescopes and learned how they were constructed, and before long he began grinding lenses and building telescopes of his own. He developed an eager appetite for reading matter that could expand his knowledge of many areas of science, including mathematics. And when he had absorbed all the mathematics of his day, he began devising new, more advanced systems of his own.

A few of Newton's notebooks remain today. Although they indicate the phenomenal breadth of his interests, they barely reflect the intensity of his thinking—of his continuous seeking and solving. Once when asked how he attacked whatever problem happened to be presented to him, he replied simply that he thought about the problem constantly until he could produce an answer to it. His powers of concentration were such that he would often work straight through the night, allowing neither fatigue nor futility to slow down his exhaustive mental activity.

While still a student, Newton observed the stars with his telescopes, experimented with various lenses, and began making notes on what was to evolve as his theory of light and color. In August, 1665, when Newton was at Cambridge, deeply involved with these experiments, bubonic plague broke out in London. This was a relatively frequent occurrence—in England as well as on the Continent—for the flea-bearing rats that carried plague found a ready haven in many squalid and congested European cities. During one plague outbreak in the twelfth century, a fourth of the population of Europe had perished. In London, in the summer of 1665, thirty-one thousand plague victims died.

When the disease began to creep beyond the confines of London, Cambridge University was closed, and all the students and masters were sent home. Newton, who had recently received his bachelor's degree, packed his telescopes and notebooks and returned to Woolsthorpe. From August, 1665, until March, 1667, the plague alternately increased and abated. During most of this time Newton was at Woolsthorpe, working as intently as he had at Cambridge. His activities covered a broad area, and the results of his experiments established the basis for most of his future scientific achievements.

He told none of his colleagues about the work he was engaged in or of the progress he was making. It seemed senseless to him to divulge any of his theories until irrefutable proof of their validity had been established. Also it would have been out of character for him to have publicized his work: even as a young man, Newton was not the kind of person to tell anyone much of anything.

One definition of genius is the infinite capacity for painstaking detail. Newton's careful study of light, which he

After many years of grinding lenses and experimenting with light rays, Newton built a new kind of telescope in 1667. Whereas Galileo's instrument had been a long tube in which light was refracted from one lens near the opening at the front to an eyepiece lens at the opposite end, Newton's design called for a shorter tube (A), a large mirror (B), a small mirror (C), and an eyepiece lens (D). Named a reflecting telescope, it did indeed reflect light from the large mirror up to the smaller one (a distance of about 6 1/3 inches) and thus achieved a sharp concentration of light. The model shown here could be focused by the thumbscrew (E).

PHOTO BY ERICH LESSING, MAGNUM

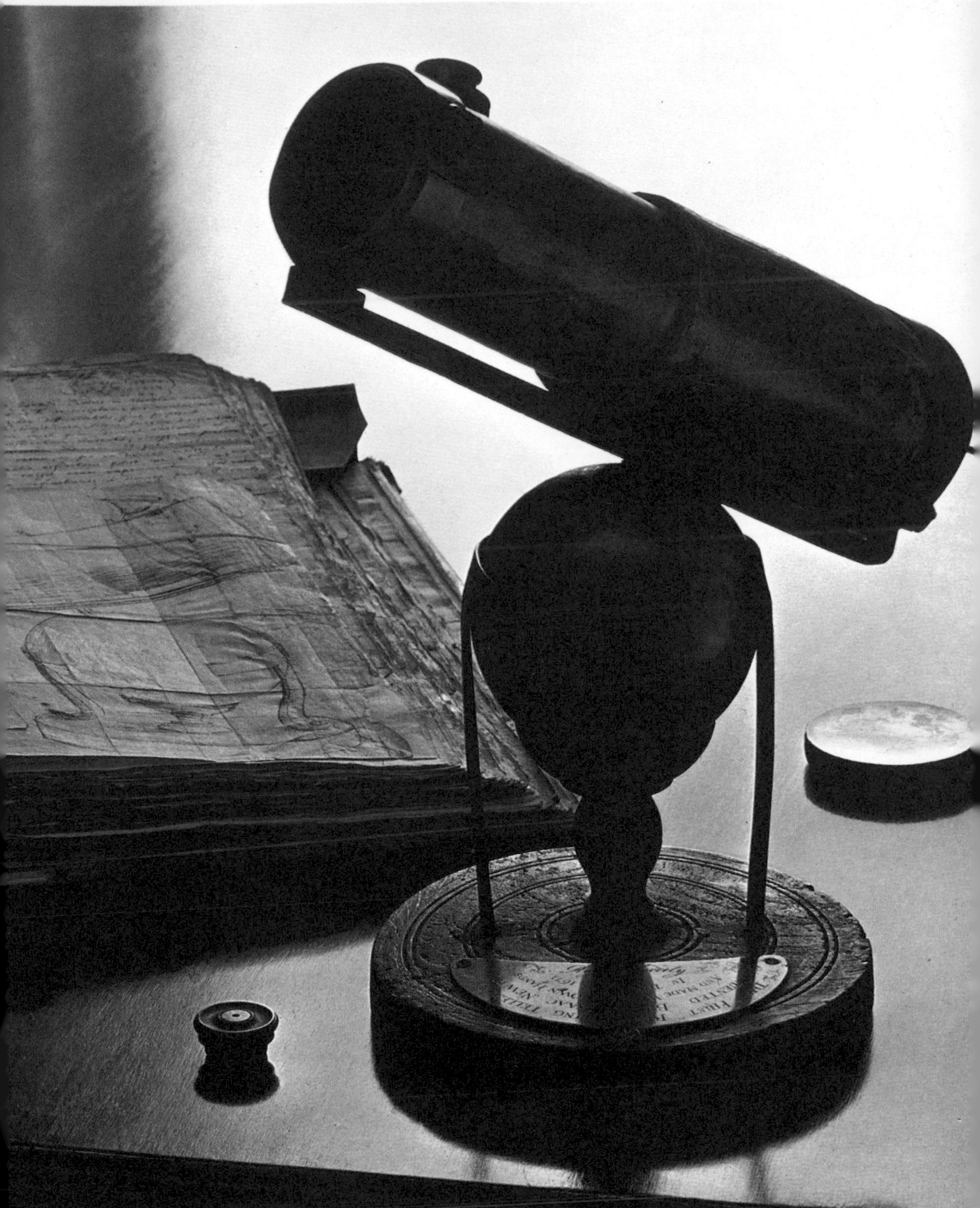

began during the plague period, nobly supports this idea. His instruments were simple, some of them primitive. He used prisms, reflecting screens, and window screens with but one or two narrow slits that would admit controllably narrow rays of sunlight.

Beyond Newton's initial interest in the phenomenon of light, he was prompted by annoyance and frustration to investigate it further. He had ground lenses for his telescopes with extreme care but had not been able to bring objects into precise focus—at least not so precise as he had wished. He began to suspect that the blurry fringes of color that outlined the images he saw through his telescopes were not caused by any imperfections in his lenses or in the glass from which they were ground. No, he reasoned, the bothersome optical defect could not be corrected because it was caused by the light itself.

Slowly, methodically, he performed scores of experiments and recorded his results. He used single prisms and prisms in combinations; he measured angles through which various colors were bent—refracted—in passing through prisms; he measured images cast on the reflecting screens; and from all these data he drew his conclusions.

As a result of one crucial experiment, he became convinced that pure sunlight itself contained a whole rainbow of colors. Using a prism, he separated a beam of sunlight into a spectrum of color that he captured on a screen. Then he placed a second prism in the path of light emerging from the first. By turning the second prism until all the colored rays entered one side of it, he observed that the light that had gone through both prisms was again pure white. Thus he had shown that all visible colors were con-

At left is a replica of the reflecting telescope Newton demonstrated to the Royal Society. An eyepiece and a mirror are on the tabletop. At right, Newton's sketch of an experiment illustrates how light coming from a small hole at far right is made to pass through a lens, a prism that separates the colors, a screen with holes for isolating the rays further, and a second prism.

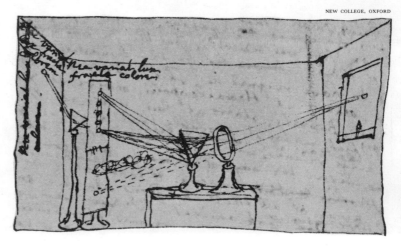

tained in sunlight—and, further, that white light could be reproduced by combining lights of many colors.

Newton also ascertained that one portion of the light passing through a lens was refracted a certain degree, and that another portion was refracted another degree. Thus, no single lens could possibly bring all the colors contained in white sunlight together at a single point. Today this defect is called chromatic aberration, and it can indeed be corrected. Most camera enthusiasts are aware of a compensating device known as an achromatic (colorless) lens, which overcomes the difficulty to some extent by using two different kinds of glass to form a lens.

But Newton did not know this. He was aware only of

The famous rainbow landscape below was painted by the Flemish artist Peter Paul Rubens. Newton, who was Rubens' contemporary, saw color with the eye of a scientist. He bought his first prism, like the one photographed at right, at a fair.

what caused the chromatic aberration that distorted his telescopic image. And to end the frustration that had produced his lengthy experimentation, he built a reflecting telescope. In this device, which he developed in 1668, he used a curved mirror instead of a lens to bring the light from distant stars into precise focus.

When he finally recognized the desirability of informing the Royal Society of his reflecting telescope, he was sincerely stunned by the amount of excitement it created, and at first he was quite pleased. Formerly, the white light from the sun had been considered pure and perfect, like Aristotle's spheres; the idea that it was made up of light of many colors was strange and puzzling. The society suggested that Newton could prevent anyone from making a false claim on his discovery by explaining it in detail and by having his papers registered in the society's records. Also, he was immediately made a candidate for society membership.

The recognition and the flattery bestowed by that body of distinguished scientists brought a quick and warm response from Newton. He had been regarded for so long as a mere outsider and a very junior member of the scientific fraternity that he could hardly believe he was being recognized as a scientist of national renown. He wrote to

When Newton was nineteen, in 1662, he made the computations above, probably after reading Euclid and Descartes. These shorthand notes may be the basis for calculus, the mathematical system he devised while he was still a student.

Henry Oldenburg, secretary of the society, to express appreciation for having been made a candidate for membership. And, he said, if he were ultimately elected to the society, he would "endeavor to testify my gratitude by communicating what my poor and solitary endeavors can effect towards promoting your philosophical designs."

Newton continued his "poor and solitary endeavors" and produced a second reflecting telescope, which he sent to the Royal Society in December, 1671, shortly before he was elected a fellow in the organization. By this time, Isaac Barrow had relinquished the coveted Lucasian chair of mathematics at Cambridge to his illustrious pupil, and Newton had already taught three courses on optics at the university. The young scientist's most intensive work had taken place during this period. But though he held his tutor in high esteem, he was so solitary and taciturn in his habits that Barrow had never received a hint of what he was working on.

Only his election as a fellow of the Royal Society, and the society's enthusiasm for his reflecting telescope, penetrated Newton's reserve. These encouragements made him uncharacteristically eager to send news of his discoveries to Secretary Oldenburg in London. Obviously he did not expect his theories to be accepted without question by the society—he must have realized that as he was barely thirty years old, he might be regarded as an upstart by some members. But Newton could not have foreseen that his paper would be greeted by a storm of opposition, most of which would come from one particular member, the intractable Robert Hooke.

Hooke was only seven years older than Newton and was almost equally brilliant. Born fragile and underdeveloped, as Newton had been, he possessed the added handicap of physical deformity. He was a temperamental man, suspicious, and jealous of his work. Unlike Newton, he did not focus his attention on a limited number of specific efforts; he would plunge into one field of research—and often make some startling discoveries—then abandon it in favor of some other project.

Hooke was called upon to be the Royal Society's curator. One of his tasks was to devise and conduct different kinds of experiments before each weekly meeting. Although this suited his agile mind, it made Hooke even less inclined to stay with a line of inquiry long enough to make a major contribution to natural science. Rarely did he complete a project he began, but he did display more than passing interest in the study of light. In his *Micrographia*, published in 1665, he reported in detail on the experiments he had made. Although Newton had begun his study of light before the *Micrographia* was published, Hooke could not help regarding Newton's theory on light as a refutation of his own. It was inevitable that the two young men should clash.

On February 8, 1672, Newton's *New Theory about Light and Colors* was read before the Royal Society. In response, the society published an order "that the author be solemnly thanked in the name of the society for this very ingenious discourse and be made acquainted that the society think very fit, if he consents to have it forthwith printed, as well for the greater convenience of having it well considered by philosophers, as for securing the considerable notices thereof to the author against the arrogations of others." Also contained in the order was a request that "the discourse be entered in the register book" and that three prominent men be asked "to peruse and consider it," among them Robert Hooke.

Newton was pleased initially by the society's reception of his paper—his contribution was evidently worthy of special treatment. But a few days later, when Hooke's report was submitted, it became clear how deeply Newton was resented. Hooke seemed to be accusing Newton of demanding that the traditional scientists of the day change their scientific methods and adopt his. In his paper Newton had disregarded all current theories and had drawn conclusions solely from the results of his private experiments.

Years before, Galileo had done much the same thing—which had angered the followers of Aristotle's theoretical approach to science. Nor had this approach been altered much by the time Newton began publishing his theories. Men like Hooke continued to follow the traditional pattern of making superficial observations of phenomena and then trying to fit them to a currently accepted hypothesis. Even the great French natural philosopher René Descartes, who was born half a century before Newton, had adhered to the accepted Aristotelian approach when he advanced his well-received thesis on the nature of light.

After Robert Hooke had examined Newton's paper, he wrote a report which he read before the society. His report said in part: "I have perused the discourse of Mr. Newton about color and refractions, and I was not a little pleased with the niceness and curiosity of his observations. But . . . as to his hypothesis of solving the phenomena of color thereby, I confess I cannot see yet any undeniable argu-

This portrait of Henry Oldenburg shows the secretary of the Royal Society dressed in Puritan garb.

ment to convince me of the certainty thereof."

The key words in this statement were "hypothesis" and "argument." For Hooke was not yet willing to accept the fact that Newton was not offering a hypothesis; he was simply stating the results of his experiments and explaining what they had proved. To Hooke, and to many men of the Royal Society, such detachment was so cold-blooded they shrank from it instinctively. Neither Newton's method nor his explanatory theory was to find easy acceptance.

Officially the Royal Society could only express dismay at the content of Newton's paper and at Hooke's rebuttal. Hooke's report was accepted and registered in the records, and a copy of it was sent to Newton. At the same time the society voted that "the printing of Mr. Newton's discovery by itself might go on if he did not contradict it; and Mr. Hooke's paper might be printed afterwards, it not being

England's Royal Society was established in 1660. Its spiritual founder was Sir Francis Bacon (right), the eminent scholar and diplomat who was Galileo's contemporary. In the engraving above, Bacon is seated on the right of the bust of King Charles II, the society's patron. Lord Brouncker, first president of the society is at left of the bust; Newton was president from 1703 to 1727.

thought fit to print them together lest Mr. Newton should look on it as a disrespect in printing so sudden a refutation of a discourse of his, which had met with so much applause at the society but a few days before."

Newton was shocked when he received a copy of Hooke's report. Since he was certain that his conclusions about the nature of light were correctly drawn from his experiments, he had assumed that his paper would be just one more step toward scientific acceptance. Yet, upon re-reading Hooke's refutation, he composed himself and wrote a restrained response to Secretary Oldenburg:

I received yours of February 18. And having considered Mr. Hooke's observations on my discourse, am glad that so acute an objector hath said nothing that can enervate any part of it. For I am still of the same judgment and doubt not but that upon severer examination, it will be found as certain a truth as I have asserted it.

As was the custom, the Royal Society sent copies of Newton's paper to leading scientists on the Continent. Among them were the great Dutch scientist Christian Huygens and Father Ignatius Pardies, a professor at the College of Clermont in Paris. Both men wrote appreciatively to the society, but each expressed strong reservations about Newton's theory. Little by little Newton was being drawn into a controversy that he had earnestly hoped to avoid. He desired only to be let alone to continue his work. But some of the arguments raised against his theory angered him. He alternated between inner fury and patient explanation.

Only a few of his contemporary scientists, like Father Pardies, asked further explanations and argued courteously; others, like Hooke and Huygens, were far from gentle. True to his nature, Newton warmed to Father Pardies and recoiled from the harsh and illogical criticism of the others.

To Father Pardies he conveyed his definition of the true scientific method. It was the one he himself employed, the one in use today, the one few of his contemporaries understood. What he wrote remains as the foundation of all scientific inquiry: ". . . the best and safest method of philosophizing seems to be first to inquire diligently into the properties of things, and of establishing these properties by experiments, and then to proceed more slowly to hypotheses for the explanation of them."

Newton hoped he could convince his English colleagues to discard their belief that they could discover the truth of nature simply by thinking about it. Newton understood that science began and ended with experiment and with correct conclusions drawn from experiments. This was why his approach was thought to be revolutionary and why so many men argued bitterly against it.

As their anger increased they sent more and more letters of protest to the Royal Society. Secretary Oldenburg urged Newton to answer them all, but Newton found his disillusionment turning to disgust—and he refused. The controversy raged for fully three years after Newton's paper on optics was first read to the Royal Society.

Newton now questioned the wisdom of sending the results of his work to the society for publication. Not only did he shrink from the bitter attacks on his work, but he resented spending so much time answering his critics. He withdrew into himself again—content with solitary work, meditation, and experiment—and the result was nearly disastrous for science. He kept notes on whatever he did, of course, but these were written for his eyes alone; they were not complete enough to be comprehensible to others. His mind pursued its own secret goals in several fields of science without any outlet to the public. He was fascinated on the one hand with the possibility of finding answers to the obscure questions posed in the texts of biblical writers, and on the other hand with reading the strange formulas of the alchemists. Experimenting with these, he kept pursuing a method for transmuting metals to gold and a universal remedy for curing disease.

He devoted his time to mathematics and to chemistry, which had always intrigued him. And he also worked on a problem that had presented itself to him years earlier, during the plague period after his return from Cambridge. For some time then he had wondered what caused the motion of the sun, moon, and planets. Galileo and Kepler had succeeded in explaining how these bodies moved, but Newton became eager to know why.

The question had gnawed at him for weeks on end. Then one moonlit night in 1666, while he was seated beneath a tree in the orchard of his Woolsthorpe farm, his meditations were jarred by the thud of an apple falling to the ground beside him. It was a commonplace occurrence, but coming when it did, it set off a chain of thoughts that enabled Newton eventually to answer all the remaining questions about the motion of planets and stars.

A table is set as if for study in the yard of Newton's farm at Woolsthorpe. On a summer eve in 1666, seated near this spot, Newton heard an apple fall.

A FALLING APPLE

Contrary to popular notion, the falling apple did not strike Newton's skull. It did not have to. The gentle thud it made striking the ground was sufficient to start Newton thinking. Ripped loose from its twig, the apple had become a free body. The moon, which shone overhead that night, was also a free, unattached body. But though the apple had plunged to the earth when freed from the tree, the moon always maintained a steady course. Whatever force held the moon in the heavens was the same, Newton felt sure, as that which pulled the apple to earth. This paradox set the twenty-four-year-old scientist on a new path of study.

Newton had read Kepler's description of elliptical planetary orbits, and he was well aware of Copernicus' description of the sun-centered universe. He was also acquainted with Galileo's principal discoveries in the study of motion. But both Kepler and Galileo had limited themselves to picturing how things moved; they had deliberately ignored the why.

For centuries people had believed and defended Aristotle's theory that some kind of force was required to keep an object in motion. Even Newton, as he puzzled over the fallen apple, felt certain that a force had brought the object to earth. The idea of gravity had been known to Galileo and to other men of his time, but to them this force was at best mysterious and at worst unaffected by the accepted laws of nature. All other kinds of motion that men knew of required some physical contact between bodies—to make a cart move, for example, something or someone had to push it. But gravity, a powerful force that made objects fall with lightning fast acceleration, was invisible.

When Newton first pondered the problem of gravity in 1666, he was aided by the knowledge of several important facts about bodies in motion. Through the work of both Galileo and Descartes, he was aware that once set in motion an object would travel in a straight line unless

Scientists swarm about the Academy of Science and Fine Arts in Paris, one of several learned societies that invited Newton to become a member.

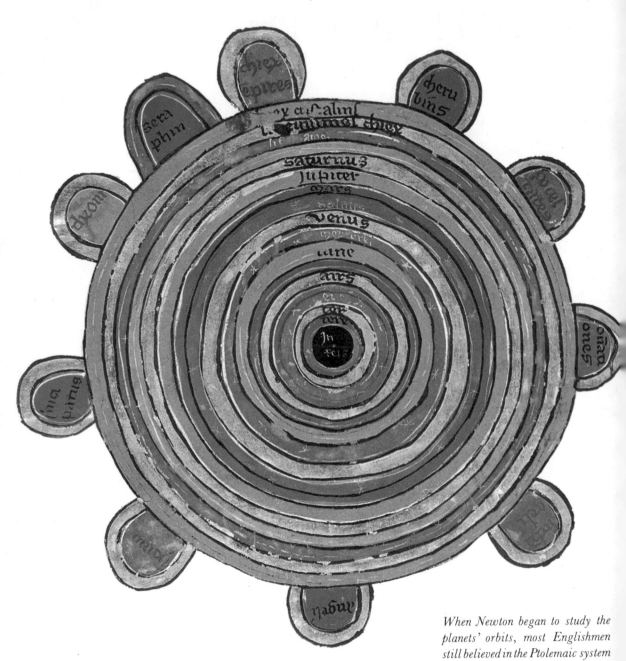

When Newton began to study the planets' orbits, most Englishmen still believed in the Ptolemaic system —as depicted in this chart of 1245. Ptolemy's universe was quite flexible, with room for both men and angels ("homo" and "angeli"); its earth-centered circles could not, however, be made to conform to observations by Kepler and Brahe.

some force intervened to turn it from its course. The moon was an object in motion, but it did not travel in a straight line. Newton came to believe that the force of gravity acted on the moon just as it did on the falling apple. It was this force, he reasoned, that caused the moon to deviate from an otherwise straight course to infinity and revolve around the earth.

Newton was certain that his logic was correct, but an important question was still to be answered. Would the force of the earth's gravity be sufficient to produce the observed orbit of the moon? Somehow he would have to determine a means for measuring the pull of gravity.

Newton suspected that the farther an object was from earth the less force was exerted on it. This, in mathematical terms, meant that the force of the earth's gravity was inversely related to the distance from earth. Defining the formula further, he reasoned that this force was not related merely to the distance itself but to the square of the distance. In practical terms, then, if an object were a hundred thousand miles from earth, the gravitational force exerted on it would be much greater than that applied to an object two hundred thousand miles away—and though the first object was half as far from earth as the second one, the force pulling it earthward would be four times as great.

This formula could only be hypothetical until Newton checked it against the path of the moon's orbit and against the distance from the moon to the earth. And since the distance covered by the force of gravity was said to begin at the very core of the earth, Newton had to determine the earth's exact radius before he could validate his other calculations. The figure he used was based on an old estimate of the earth's circumference, and since that figure was inaccurate by more than 15 per cent, Newton unknowingly obtained a faulty value for the radius.

Proceeding with his calculations, however, he tried to figure out whether the force pulling inward toward the earth would produce the existing orbit of the moon. At length he reached a fairly satisfactory and confirming conclusion, although he was thwarted by the inaccuracy of the figures he had used. While Newton could not account for the error at that time, he was reasonably certain he had come close to achieving a solution. But as there was still room for doubt, he chose not to publicize his results. He put away his notes on gravitation, and for the next fifteen years one of the greatest of all scientific ideas remained buried and ignored.

TEXT CONTINUED ON PAGE 111

The high and paneled hall of Trinity College, Cambridge, where Newton lectured is at right; on the end wall is a portrait of King Henry VIII, founder of the college. As in his own time, Newton is still revered at Cambridge; the university's finest work of art is a sculpture of him (above). The poet Wordsworth called it "Newton with the prism and silent face."

In his efforts to measure the exact speed of sound, Newton experimented with echoes at Trinity College in this long arcade called the Cloisters.

TEXT CONTINUED FROM PAGE 107

It was during these years (1666–81) that his experiments with light were concluded and his distressing controversy with the Royal Society began. His bitterness and hostility toward the Royal Society reached such a peak that in 1673 he asked to be dropped from its rolls. Secretary Oldenburg refused to accept Newton's resignation. As he was aware of the reason for Newton's actions, Oldenburg wrote him reassuringly, "You may be satisfied that the [membership] in general esteems and loves you . . ." Newton was relieved of any financial obligation to the society, and though he remained on its rolls, he was for all practical purposes an inactive member.

At Cambridge where he continued to live and work, legends about him began to grow. To some students he was the personification of an absent-minded professor. He was careless in his manner of dress, often appearing before his students in a state of disarray. He was unconcerned with externals—so much so that even if nobody attended one of his classes, he would deliver his lecture with as much satisfaction as if the hall had been crowded with listeners.

With or without an audience, he delivered one lecture a week, which, according to custom, was filed in the university library. The weeks passed, and the years, and Newton's sphere of scientific interest expanded. He set up a laboratory in Cambridge where he spent long hours poring over a variety of scientific problems.

By 1678, within a short span of time, both his former tutor Isaac Barrow and Henry Oldenburg died. In Oldenburg's place the society elected two men to handle the correspondence and plan the meetings. One of these men was Robert Hooke. In the spirit of amity, Hooke wrote to Newton at Cambridge. His letter contained news of activities in the scientific world, and a query: what, if anything, could Newton contribute to the advancement of the Royal Society?

Newton did not wish to be drawn into the swirl of discussion and debate that previous remarks of his had touched off. So in replying to Hooke he wrote simply that he was involved in "other business" and hoped the society would forgive his lack of interest. Then, possibly because of the guilt he felt about his refusal, Newton outlined an experiment that Hooke or anyone might try. The object of the experiment was to determine the path of a falling body toward the center of the earth. When he had finished the letter, Newton probably hoped to hear no more from Hooke. He could not have been more mistaken.

TEXT CONTINUED ON PAGE 114

Coffee houses had become the focal point of male society by Newton's time, although t... first one had only opened its doors in 1650. In this painting of the interior of a cof...

...use, a waiter (at left) collects pipes and tobacco bowls to serve to the bewigged
...trons, who seem more interested in smoking and debating than in drinking coffee.

TRINITY COLLEGE, CAMBRIDGE

In Newton's 1679 letter to the Royal Society (above) he outlined a suggested experiment. Robert Hooke found an error in the sketch.

TEXT CONTINUED FROM PAGE 111

Hooke read the proposed experiment before the society membership, and he himself became quite interested in it. But looking at the rough sketch that Newton had included to illustrate his point, Hooke discovered an error.

Immediately Hooke wrote back to Newton, pointing out the mistake. Nothing was more likely to further anger and estrange Newton. But his response to Hooke, though brusque and cool, only furthered Hooke's interest. Hooke was delighted by his own display of knowledge. He was also eager to pursue the experiment Newton had suggested, and he bombarded Newton with letters about it.

One result of this barrage was that Newton finally became so enraged that he refused to respond at all. Another, and more far-reaching result was that Newton was so stung by the discovery of the error in his sketch that he soon returned to the problem of gravitation.

In his early calculations Newton had measured earth's gravitational effect on the moon by estimating that sixty statute miles were equal to one degree of latitude. But this had produced an error of about 15 per cent in his calculations. Recently it had been proved that sixty nautical miles were also equal to one degree of latitude. Newton saw that the nautical mile, with which global measurements are computed, was about 15 per cent greater than the statute mile. Recalling his original figures, he set to work replacing the statute mile with the nautical mile. Using his corrected data, his error would nearly vanish, and he knew he would finally have the mathematical proof that the force of gravity extended to the moon.

Reportedly, Newton became so excited at the prospect of finding an accurate solution to the problem of the moon's orbit that in the final phases of his calculation his hands began to shake. It is said that he had to give his notes to a friend who was with him because he could not complete the arithmetic himself.

The excitement did not last, however, and Newton characteristically put his proof away in a drawer that contained many other notes. Although he had answered one great question about gravitation, he already suspected that several more would have to be answered before a complete paper on the subject could be written. If his concept of gravity was correct, he wondered, what would be the path of one object revolving about another, as the planets do about the sun? Would it be an ellipse? as Kepler had believed—and why?

The moon, as he had pictured it, was just like any other

falling body: once set in motion, it tended to fly off in a straight line—except that its course was bent into a curve because of the effect of the earth's gravity. In formulating this theory, Newton had made a combination of the laws of inertia—which had been conceived by Galileo and finally expressed by Descartes—and Kepler's laws of motion. With this combination, and his own insight, Newton could finally answer the why of planetary motion.

He conceived of a universe in which all heavenly bodies possessed strong forces that attracted one another. Though the system was harmonious, the sun, being the largest body, dominated the system, drawing all the subordinate bodies in elliptical orbits around it.

When he was satisfied that his solution was correct,

PHOTO BY CHRISTOPHER ANGELOGLOU

The Mathematical Bridge spans a canal at Queen's College, Cambridge. Newton designed it so all its beams were self-bracing and needed no nails.

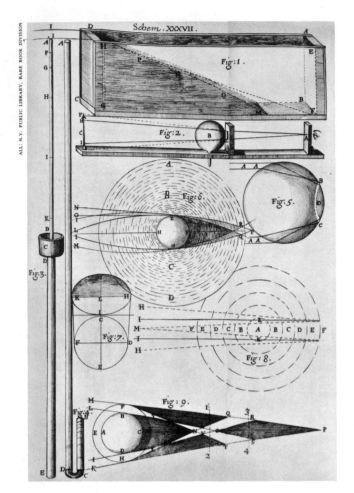

Like Galileo, Robert Hooke (1635–1703) was a ceaseless experimenter and a fiery debater. At left are his drawings of the equipment he used to determine the nature of light: tubes, spheres, a shadow box, and a sighting device. He concluded that light has some of the oscillating qualities of waves. Above is a microscope that he designed; a spherical condenser focuses light from the oil lamp onto a specimen.

Newton once again stopped pondering the planets and turned back to the study of light. But other men found it impossible to dismiss thoughts of the universe now that rumors and echoes of new theories were being circulated. One day in January, 1684, three important members of the Royal Society met in a London coffee house. They were Robert Hooke, a young astronomer named Edmund Halley, and the noted astronomer and supreme architect of his time, Sir Christopher Wren. They met, as men of similar interests are wont to do, to discuss issues in which they were mutually concerned. Their conversation turned to the still unsolved question of gravitational force and to Kepler's laws of planetary motion. Like other scientists, the three men believed that the inverse-square law pertaining to distance and gravity was true, and they further believed that this law somehow produced the planets' elliptical orbits, but they could not substantiate their beliefs.

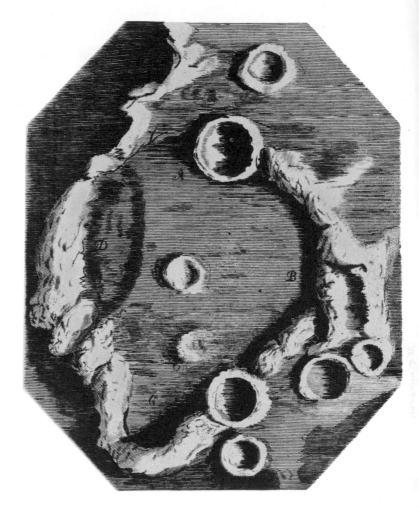

Hooke was also a competent astronomer; he was the first to state that the revolutions of the planets were a mechanical problem. His 1664 drawing of an area on the moon is at right. Of this observation he wrote: "Inside A B C D is a spacious vale, encompassed with a ridge of hills [having] the shape of a pear . . . Surface appears to be covered with a vegetable substance like our grass . . . and trees."

At one point in the discussion, Hooke declared flatly that he could prove the inverse-square law and that when the time came he would present his evidence. Hooke spoke with his customary certitude, but Wren was not easily won over. He asked why Hooke did not produce the necessary figures immediately. Hooke insisted that the time was not ripe. Besides, he said, if he did bring Wren the desired proof, someone else would probably make a prior claim on it.

It was an audacious boast, as both Wren and Halley were probably aware. But Hooke's fear of a prior claim was not unjustified. The late seventeenth century was a time of heightened scientific activity and much competition. All over Europe and in England there was a stirring that indicated the approach of what might today be called a breakthrough in the quest for new knowledge of the physical universe. Robert Boyle had begun to organize the results of years of patient labor into what is now known as the science of chemistry. New knowledge of the behavior of light resulted in heated arguments among such scientists as Hooke, Newton, and Christian Huygens. And the English astronomer John Flamsteed was at the newly built Greenwich observatory taking what was to be the most accurate observation ever made of the stars. The question of gravitation was being discussed by scientists everywhere. The three men seated in that coffee house in London were but part of a rising wave of wonder.

Wren listened skeptically to Hooke's claim and then offered a prize—a book worth forty shillings—to anyone who could submit mathematical proof that gravitational force acting on a planet would make it orbit in an elliptical path. Further, he said that whoever brought him this proof would have his claim of discovery recorded and published and that therefore neither Hooke nor anyone else need fear losing the fame that went with winning the prize.

When Wren had finished, Halley smiled and shook his head. He too would try, but he did not think he could supply the required proof. Hooke, on the other hand,

The two formally dressed gentlemen above helped bring forth Newton's proof for the elliptical shape of orbits. Edmund Halley (at right) persuaded Newton to make the computations. Christian Huygens (at left), a Dutch physicist, had made mathematical analyses of circular motion in Paris.

assured both men that he already had it and that he would come forward shortly to claim the prize.

Wren had placed a two months' time limt on his offer, but even after several weeks had passed, Hooke did not come forward. Nor was Halley successful in finding a solution to the problem. At the end of the allotted period, Halley looked to Hooke to disclose his mathematical solution, but still Hooke was silent.

Halley was disappointed. To him the prize was of secondary importance; he was eager only to see the problem solved. Finally he decided to take some action. Late in the summer of 1684 he told Wren that he was going to Cambridge to see Isaac Newton. If any man on earth could solve the problem, he said, Newton could.

So he journeyed to Cambridge and confronted Newton in his study. Without wasting time, the young astronomer asked what would be the path of a planet under a gravitational attraction that varied inversely as the square of the distance from the sun. Unhesitatingly Newton replied, "An ellipse."

Halley then asked how Newton knew this, and the older scientist replied, in characteristic understatement, "I have calculated it." Greatly excited, Halley asked if he could see the calculations. Newton searched half-heartedly among his research material but could not locate the notes. After all, it had been five years since he had solved the problem of the moon's falling, and since then his mind had been occupied with other matters.

Newton apologized to the unhappy Halley and promised to rework the problem and send the results to London. Halley's visit provided the stimulus Newton needed to resume work on the general study of why things move. If Halley had not come, Newton might never have brought his old calculations back from limbo for many years more. As it was, he reworked his solution, and in November, 1684, sent his proof to Halley.

Doubtless, Halley was awed by Newton's precise mathematical solution. On scraps of paper covered with Newton's scribbled notations, Halley at last held the answer to the question of why the planets move as they do about the sun. Newton was obviously an extraordinary man. Not only had he made an extremely important discovery, but he had made it years before and had not bothered to tell anyone about it. Halley made a hurried return trip to Cambridge to urge Newton to set down everything he had discovered about motion.

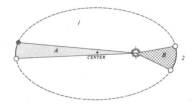

Planetary orbits, as correctly described by Kepler in 1609, are elliptical—that is, football-shaped. One focus of the ellipse is the sun (which is located at a point halfway between the center and one tip of the ellipse). The speed of the planet varies as it whips around the orbit: it covers distance number 1 in the same length of time as distance number 2, assuming that the areas A and B are the same size.

Flattered by Halley's admiration, and prodded by the younger man's earnestness, Newton agreed to write a short paper on the subject. Halley returned again to London, secure in the knowledge that Newton's achievement would make astronomy one of the most exacting of sciences and that his fame could never again be challenged. If the deadline had not been past, he clearly would have been awarded the forty-shilling prize as well as honors. from all the scientific world. With Newton's gravitational law, combined with Kepler's laws of planetary motion, astronomers would now be able to extend their knowledge into the universe, even beyond the immediately observable planets.

For although a new age of science was dawning in England and on the Continent, there was but scant understanding of the true design of the universe. Comets, for example, remained a completely puzzling factor. No one, not even Newton, had been able to account for their random appearance and erratic behavior. Since ancient times these strange bodies had excited and frightened people all over the world. At unpredictable times, and for reasons unknown, comets had appeared suddenly, lingering for perhaps several days within view of earth, and then had vanished. Such was the case in 1680.

That year most people thought they had seen two comets. Astronomers in Europe had trained their telescopes on the comets to study them, while common folk everywhere spoke in hushed tones of the heavenly omens of

The search for a formula to prove that gravitational force produces elliptical orbits was initiated by Sir Christopher Wren and successfully concluded by Newton. Better known as an architect than an astronomer, Wren stands in the portrait at right with his most famous building, St. Paul's Cathedral, in the background. At left is the library that was designed by Wren and constructed at Cambridge during Newton's years there. Built in the neo-classical style that recalls the Italian Renaissance, it has one special alcove that today contains Newton's personal library.

disaster. At the observatory in Greenwich, John Flamsteed recorded the positions of the comets periodically as they moved through the sky. He concluded that they followed elliptical paths, similar to but longer than those of the planets. He realized further that the two comets that had been sighted that year were really only one. It had first appeared during one part of its orbit. Then after passing around the sun, it had reappeared later and was thought to be another comet.

For years a number of obstacles had prevented the true understanding of comets. The greatest of these obstacles had been the inability to make a precise observation of their orbits. Flamsteed's painstaking work had overcome this hurdle, but another obstacle lay in the fact that the paths of comets are so extended that many comets are visible on earth only once in the course of a human lifetime. Without systematically checking old records, no one would know that the appearance of a comet is periodic, hence predictable.

Newton himself believed that there had been two comets in 1680. It was not until many years had passed that he became convinced that comets, like planets, moved in elliptical paths and responded to the same law of gravitation that the planets obeyed. But it was Halley himself who, putting Newton's law of gravitation to practical use, later demonstrated that comets moved in paths resembling elongated ellipses and even parabolas. His exhaustive study of comets, and of the records of their appearance, led him to the discovery of the comet that now bears his name. Halley's Comet, last seen in 1910, has been shown to reappear every seventy-five years.

Newton's proof that gravitational attraction controlled the moon's path and the movement of planets about the sun was an unquestioned triumph for astronomy. But most other scientists, while acknowledging the importance of this proof, believed that its application was limited. No one suspected the extent to which Newton wished to apply his principle. While astronomers were satisfied to use his principle of gravitation in their work, Newton saw in it much more usefulness than anyone else had imagined.

The woodcut at right above shows a comet startling German townspeople in 1680. The most active English chronicler of comets was John Flamsteed, who worked at the Royal Observatory (above) designed by Wren. To provide many walls with windows, Wren planned a large octagonal room (right).

VII

THE PRINCIPIA

The work of Copernicus and Galileo had destroyed the whole structure of Aristotelian physics. But one of Aristotle's precepts about the physical universe remained unchallenged: the persistent notion that there was a difference between occurrences on earth and those elsewhere in the universe. Imperfect men lived on an imperfect earth, the Greek philosopher had declared; perfection was to be found in the heavens. Thus, Aristotle had reasoned, the laws governing earthly happenings could not possibly apply to the heavens.

But this theory too, which still appealed to thinkers of the seventeenth century, was soon to be exploded. In his quiet study at Cambridge, Newton was working carefully toward a scientific masterpiece that would overshadow the work of any previous scientist. His first objective, prompted by Halley, was to fashion one precise mathematical statement about gravity that would account not only for the motions of planets but for the fall of an apple from a tree and the course of a bullet from a rifle barrel.

Years before, Galileo had studied the path of a projectile. It neither fell abruptly nor soared endlessly into space; its route across the sky could be charted somewhere between the two dissimilar motions that Newton would one day study—the moon that fell constantly but never came to rest, and the apple that plunged directly earthward. Perhaps the projectile's route was a combination of both of these motions, Galileo concluded: the path of any projectile hurled upward at an angle—be it an arrow or a cannon ball—must surely be curved in the form of a parabola. He was correct, more or less. He would have been totally correct if he had seen that the problem was not a

N.Y. PUBLIC LIBRARY, RARE BOOK DIVISION

Early cannoneers worked out the elevation of their bombards with the quadrant invented by Galileo.

A year before Isaac Newton's death, when he was eighty-four, this portrait was made by Johann Vanderbank; by then, religion was Newton's chief concern.

125

Medieval physicists thought that impetus carried a missile upwards in a straight line until gravity overcame impetus and the missile dropped straight to the ground.

matter of a missile rising up from one point on a flat surface and then falling down toward another point on that surface; the problem actually involves a missile soaring up from a sphere (the earth) and then being drawn down toward the center of that sphere. If Galileo had charted the problem this way, he would have seen that the path was not a parabola, but part of an ellipse—like a section of the moon's orbit.

Newton began to think of a missile's trajectory in this new light. He knew that its path would initially be curved, and he perceived that it would ultimately be elliptical. If an apple could be hurled with sufficient force it might go into orbit around the earth.

Here then was the crucial relationship, the relationship between natural motion and gravity, that Newton had been seeking. But to measure the force of gravity

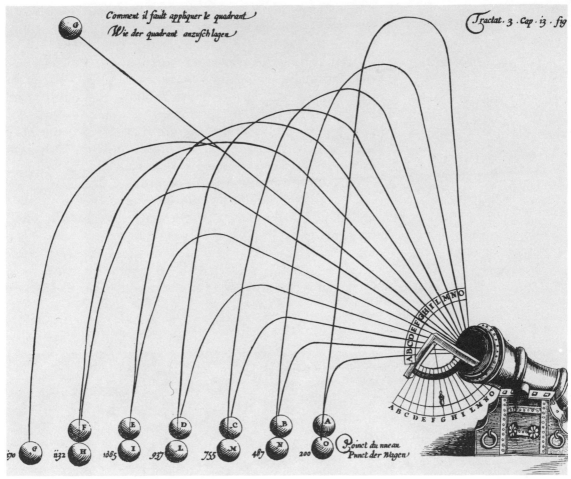

Comment il fault appliquer le quadrant
Wie der quadrant anzuschlagen

Tractat. 3 . Cap . 13 . fig

This diagram from a gunner's handbook of 1621 shows the true parabolic path of a missile. The shot marked G has been fired at the ideal 45° angle for long distance.

that was constantly drawing an object toward or around the earth, he had to establish a trustworthy way of measuring the distances involved. When trying to gauge the forces acting on the falling apple, for example, should measurements be made merely from the apple's skin to the grass below, or from the core of the apple to the earth's center? Instinctively he answered that the proper figure was the distance between the center of the earth and the center of the apple. He did so on the same impulse that would prompt anyone desiring to balance a plate on one finger to place his finger at the center of the plate. Yet he was not satisfied with just an instinctive solution. Too many of these had been proved wrong. Applying his vast knowledge of mathematics, he set out to show that the combined gravitational effect on the apple of every cubic foot of earth—

127

that beneath his feet and that on the opposite side of the earth—was exactly the same as though the entire bulk of the earth were concentrated at the center.

Completing this stupendous calculation, Newton knew that he finally had within his grasp a single statement that related heavenly motions to those on earth. And if he could express it accurately, it would overshadow any purely philosophical description of the universe, such as that of Aristotle's. Previously Newton had given astronomers useful information in relating the planets' elliptical orbits to the pull of gravity. Now he could offer to all other scientists who were concerned with force and motion on the earth a precise and irrefutable law about how gravity acts and why objects move as they do. Newton's law of universal gravitation states: "Every particle in the universe is attracted to every other particle by a force that is directly related to the products of their masses

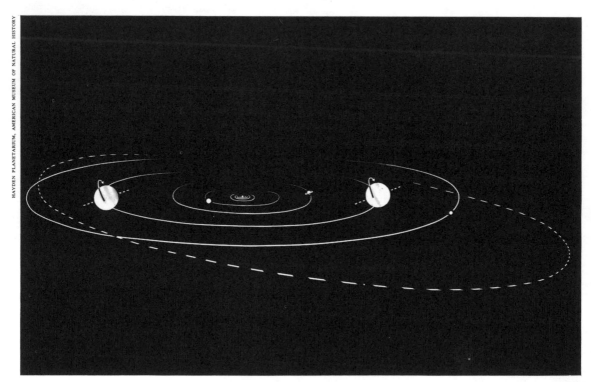

HAYDEN PLANETARIUM, AMERICAN MUSEUM OF NATURAL HISTORY

The course of the planets across the sky became in Newton's mind a mechanical problem. Diagramed above are the nine neatly meshing orbits of the solar system. The planets revolve concentrically and in roughly the same plane; only Pluto's orbit (dotted line) is markedly inclined. And only the axis of Uranus (the large sphere) is severely tilted from the vertical.

Many men in Newton's day and subsequent generations considered his concept of a mechanical universe inhuman and repellent. William Blake (1757–1827), the noted English poet and artist, made this extremely uncomplimentary drawing of Newton as a devilish draftsman.

and inversely related to the squares of the distances between them." Thus, for two boxes hanging two inches apart from a beam, the force pulling them towards each other would be determined by dividing the product of their masses by the distance squared, that is, four inches.

Newton had found the formula that unraveled the mystery of the physical universe, and he knew it. Yet such was his nature that, finished with the problem and privately satisfied with its solution, he did not announce his revolutionary discovery. Instead he perfected his mathematical proof and arranged the material in a series of lectures which he delivered to his Cambridge classes. It is possible that he would have placed the text of his lectures in a file, once his classes were over, and turned his attention to other things. But he had promised to send Halley a report on the results of his work, so instead of merely storing his lectures, he dispatched copies of them to London.

At first, Halley was puzzled. He had left Newton at work on a problem in astronomy—or what might be called celestial mechanics. Yet here was a treatise relating motions on earth with celestial motions—motions everywhere, in fact. Though he did not grasp its entire significance at first, Halley had a suspicion that the paper contained a monumental discovery. He presented the paper to the Royal Society on December 10, 1684, and the minutes note the receipt of that "curious treatise." It was obvious that

the Newton paper was of great importance, but it would have to receive further study.

Meanwhile Halley urged Newton to expand the paper and to prepare a book for publication. It is likely that without Halley's urging, Newton would never have undertaken to publish. Certainly he had no enthusiasm for the task; his past experience had drained that from him. But Halley's tact and good humor won him over. He set out to produce a small book that would set forth his proof of the law of gravitational force, show how it related to Kepler's laws of planetary motion, and also include some geometrical theorems that related to the subject.

He put aside other work and began to fulfill his promise to Halley. But as Newton developed his idea and began to illustrate it with examples, he realized the extent of what he must write, and the book grew larger and larger.

At his room in Cambridge, his very life was consumed by the book. Meals remained uneaten. Sleep was avoided —he often worked until three or four in the morning, only to rise again soon after dawn. Newton's housekeeper complained, for it appeared that Newton did not like her cooking. Many times all Newton ate was bread and water —just enough nourishment to keep his mental machinery functioning. He was so preoccupied with his work that he seldom left his room. And when he did, he appeared in the college halls with wig awry and stockings hanging down. He seemed completely detached from worldly problems, as though his mind were billions of miles from earth —which indeed it was.

By Easter time, 1685, Newton had finished one volume of what was to be a three-volume work. By late summer, the second volume was nearly completed. He spent a great deal of time revising and polishing his material, so that it was not until springtime, 1686, that he allowed the first volume to be sent to the Royal Society in London.

The manuscript was titled *Philosophiae Naturalis Principia Mathematica* ("Mathematical Principles of Natural Philosophy"), but has been referred to consistently as simply the *Principia*. No sooner had it been delivered to the society and been read by several members than another controversy

Upon publication of the Principia, *Newton was recognized as one of Europe's leading scientists. In the allegorical painting at left, a proud Britannia stands between the aging scientist (seated) and a young Dutch mathematician. In 1701 Newton moved to London; his house in the city is shown above.*

131

COURTESY DERBY ART GALLERY COMMITTEE, ENGLAND

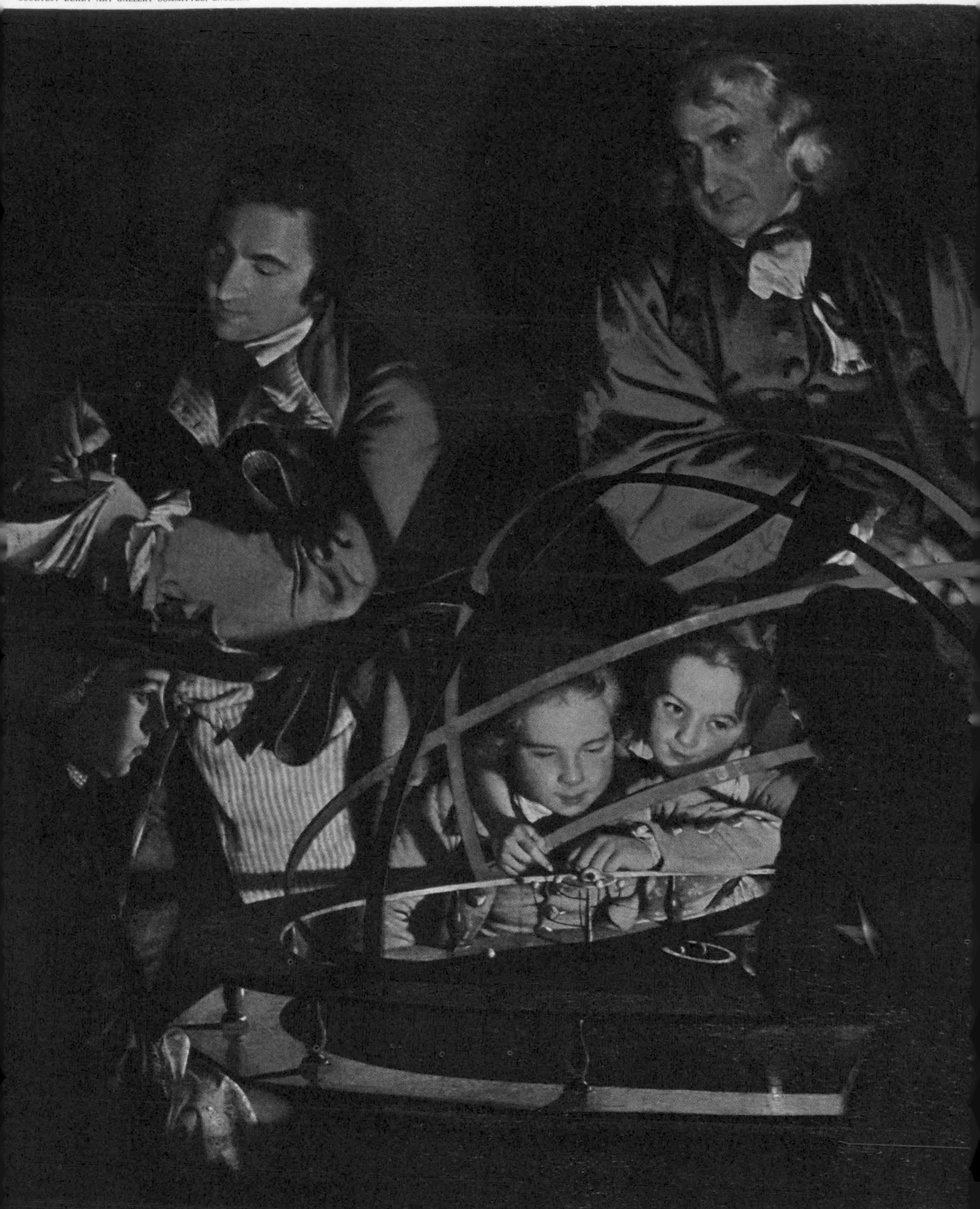

was in the making. Newton's old antagonist Robert Hooke claimed to be the discoverer of the inverse-square law and accused Newton of including it in the *Principia* without acknowledging Hooke's priority.

The Royal Society was embarrassed, and several key members openly expressed their dismay. They knew that this kind of controversy could halt Newton's work. But Hooke remained adamant. It was true, of course, that Hooke had guessed that gravity could be measured by an inverse-square law. Other scientists, including Halley and Wren, had guessed it too, but no one until Newton could supply mathematical proof that the law was valid. Hooke was demanding credit for a discovery he had never been able to substantiate.

Halley was determined to be the first to inform Newton of the difficulty, and he did so immediately. He knew that if the news came from another source, or if it were to become distorted, Newton would probably cease communicating with the society and that the remainder of the *Principia* might never be written. Appended to the lengthy letter that he sent to Newton was this important passage:

There is one thing more that I ought to inform you of, viz., that Mr. Hooke has some pretensions upon the invention of the rule of decreases of gravity being reciprocally as the squares of the distances from the center . . . How much of this is so, you know best; as likewise what you have to do in this matter. Only Mr. Hooke seems to expect you should make some mention of him in the preface, which it is possible you may see reason to prefix.

Newton, of course, was furious. He thanked Halley for the explanatory letter and made clear his intention of ignoring Hooke's claim. "In the papers in your hands," he wrote, "there is not one proposition to which he can pretend, and so I had no proper occasion of mentioning him there . . ."

In the midst of this delicate exchange of letters, the society decided that Newton's book should be published. Discovering that its treasury had insufficient funds for such an undertaking, the society sought independent financing. According to an entry in the minutes of the June 2, 1686, meeting, "It was ordered that Mr. New-

Following Newton's universal formulas, engineers began to build devices that accurately demonstrated the design of our solar system. Such devices came to be called orreries; one of them, equipped with a central lamp, is exhibited by a scientist to a family group in the 1765 painting at left.

Reproduced above is the title page of Newton's original manuscript of the Mathematical Principles of Natural Philosophy *(the* Principia*). Modern science began with this great work that explained much of the nature of the universe. The first of the* Principia's *three volumes is concerned with definitions, which start on this page.*

ton's book be printed, and that Mr. Halley undertake the business of looking after it and printing it at his own charge . . .''

Edmund Halley was not a man of means. Though once wealthy, his family had lost its fortune, and he had to live on a relatively small income. Still, he recognized the importance of Newton's work, and he knew that it had to be published. So he accepted the responsibility—and the obligation. It was his act of generosity, freely made, that determined the outcome of the dispute between Newton and Hooke.

Halley had been the first to bring Hooke's claim to Newton's attention, but he was not the last. After Newton had heard from a number of sources that Hooke felt slighted, he wrote to Halley that he was disgusted with the entire project. He had finished two of the three volumes, and though he had begun volume three, it was still unfinished at the time volume one was going to press. Now he said he planned to withhold the third volume.

Halley was stunned. He replied to Newton as diplomatically as possible, in the hope of calming the angry genius. His tact proved equal to the task, for with his letter, Newton's resistance softened. Newton appreciated Halley's encouragement. And aware that the young astronomer was paying the costs of publication, he could see that the sale of the completed work would be less if the third volume were omitted. Once his anger had abated, Newton wrote to Halley, "I am very sensible of the great kindness of the gentlemen of your society to me, far beyond what I could ever expect or deserve, and know how to distinguish between their favor and another's humor . . ."

Newton was feeling so conciliatory, in fact, that he even agreed to acknowledge that several other scientists, including Hooke, had deduced the inverse-square relationship between distance and gravitational force.

The *Principia* was published in the summer of 1687, and though it established Newton's fame for all times, most people who were interested in it found it impossible to fathom. The book was written in Latin, the language of scholars at that time. Also, for the benefit of scholars, the mathematical proofs were laboriously worked out in classic geometry rather than calculus. By doing this, Newton hoped that scientists would be able to understand his new ideas through the proofs. Still, few were able to shake themselves free of traditional beliefs and even glimpse the universe that Newton had accurately analyzed.

In the letter to Edmund Halley at right Newton recounts how he derived his mathematical proof for Kepler's theory of elliptical orbits many years before Robert Hooke boasted that he had the necessary data. However, Newton concludes the letter by agreeing to mention Hooke in a "scholium." With the letter are some additional geometrical diagrams that relate to the principle of universal gravitation.

For he had seen it as no man before him had been able to do.

The *Principia* did not win acceptance immediately; it took some time before men could adjust their thinking to Newton's radically new view of science. Building on Galileo's belief in thorough experimentation and on his shrewd deductions, Newton established experiment as the way of science and the only correct method of examining nature.

In the field of physics, he exposed errors that had existed—and had been compounded—for two thousand years. He forced scientists to probe deeper into nature and to discard hasty, superficial observation that so often leads to false conclusions. For example, prior to publication of the *Principia*, men believed that an object's natural state was motionlessness, or rest. In everyday observation all things seemed eventually to stop moving. Water flowed to the sea and ceased flowing; a stone rolled down a hillside and finally stopped; any object set in motion by man eventually stopped moving. Rest was seen, therefore, as an ideal state that every object sought.

By his discoveries, Newton showed that man lives in a universe in which motion is the natural state of things. His three laws of motion, set forth in the *Principia*, provide the basis of the science of mechanics. They state:

I. Every material body persists in its state of rest or uniform motion in a straight line if, and only if, it is not acted upon by an external force.

II. The net external force acting on a material object is directly and linearly proportional to, and in the same direction as, the acceleration of the object.

III. To every action there is always opposed an equal reaction.

In his first law, Newton used the word "rest" to describe the condition of an object, but for him the word had special connotations. An object lying on a table in a quiet room may be considered at rest—but only if consideration is made for the fact that the room and the object are turning as the earth turns on its axis, and both are moving with the earth in its rotation about the sun.

Newton's *Principia* contains the main body of knowledge that composes the science of mechanics, one of the major divisions of physics. Essentially, mechanics involves forces—and motions produced by forces. It is the most precise science yet conceived by man, and it is fundamental to modern life. Newtonian principles enable men to design machines and to calculate accurately the amount of energy needed to do specific jobs. They make it possible for men to build and launch a rocket so that it will blast free from the earth's gravitational influence and remain in an orbit around the earth.

The mighty seed that had grown into Isaac Newton's *Principia* was the law of universal gravitation, and that law remained a generative force in Newton's mind and in the minds of others. By means of it he presented the first satisfactory explanation of the earth's tides. But, more significantly, he established for all times a relationship between the forces on earth and those throughout the universe.

On a table beneath a bust of Newton in the Wren Library are arranged his copy of the Principia *and a working replica of his reflecting telescope.*

A full figure of Newton appears on this medal cast by the Royal Society. The inscription on it reads "For the patronage of the King by the authority of the Society."

ISAAC NEWTON, FELLOW
Given by ED BARLOW   1642-1727   RYSBRACK

BEYOND THE PLANETS

The *Principia*, published when Newton was forty-five, represented the culmination of his scientific achievement. His book called *Optics* was printed in 1704, but most of it had been written long before and summarized previous scientific and creative efforts. After the *Principia*, Newton's major work as a scientist and mathematician was essentially over.

Despite a nervous illness that kept him indisposed for about two years, he continued his professorial duties at Cambridge until 1696. That year, in recognition of his work, he was appointed warden of the mint. He retained his Cambridge offices for four years, until he became master of the mint. In 1701, he resigned his professorship and moved to London, where he resided until his death in 1727.

Honor followed honor in the years after the *Principia*. In 1703 he became president of the Royal Society, a position to which he was re-elected annually for the rest of his life. In 1705 he was knighted by Queen Anne for his services to the Crown. In 1708 he sanctioned the printing of a second edition of the *Principia*, and a third edition appeared the year before his death.

The book earned Newton considerable fame in England, but it was unenthusiastically received abroad. Men like Huygens, who had disputed Newton's early theories, remained steadfast in their criticism of him. Yet even those who criticized him felt compelled to acknowledge his greatness as a scientific figure.

Scientific skepticism about Newton's theories led to more and more experiment, as men checked and rechecked his proofs and calculations. Eventually their attempts to disprove him succeeded in proving him right. Then by

Queen Anne (above) knighted Newton in the drawing room of Trinity Lodge (right) in 1705 beneath the portrait of his great predecessor Galileo.

DIEV ET MON DROIT

applying Newton's laws and perfecting the far-seeing instruments he had invented, scientists were enabled to peer farther and deeper into the universe.

During Newton's lifetime, the farthest-known planet from the sun was Saturn. Years afterward, in 1781, an English astronomer named William Herschel discovered the planet Uranus. Then its entire orbit was plotted by means of Newton's principles, but astronomers were astonished to note that the planet frequently seemed to veer from its course. Noting Uranus' unusual perturbations (variations in a planet's orbit), some scientists suggested that Newton's law of universal gravitation might be weakened—and even made ineffective—because of the great distance between Uranus and the sun. Perturbations were expected in some areas, where one planet's path might be influenced or distorted by the others, but Uranus seemed to be behaving in a wholly unusual way. Perhaps gravitational force did not extend that far. (The orbit of Uranus swings so far from the sun that the planet requires eighty-four years to complete a single revolution.)

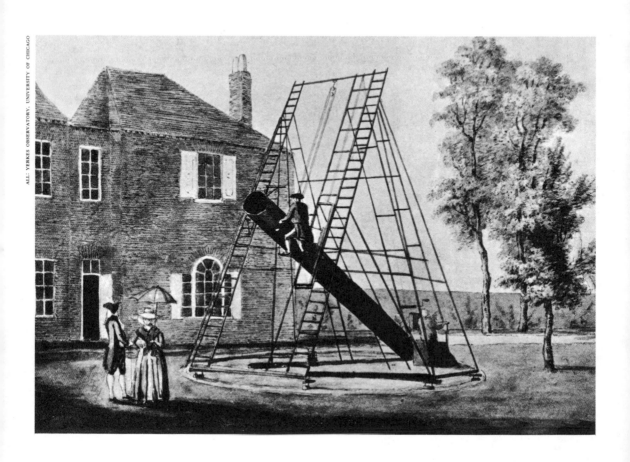

However, many scientists suspected that some force other than distance might be the difficulty. They believed that Newton's law was correct and that what caused Uranus' extreme perturbations was the presence of yet another planet—one that was still undiscovered and that lay even farther from the sun than Uranus.

After more than half a century of unsuccessful searching, two men began the immensely difficult job of calculating the probable orbit of this unknown planet. They were a French astronomer named Urbain Jean Joseph Leverrier and John C. Adams, a student who worked near Newton's old study at Cambridge University. Adams completed his calculations in 1845 and asked that the Royal Observatory in Greenwich direct its telescope toward a specific area of the heavens and begin the search. But Adams was relatively unknown, and the Royal Observatory did not do as he asked. At this time Leverrier completed his calculations and sent them to an observatory in Berlin. Both Adams and Leverrier, it developed, had predicted the appearance of a new planet in the same region of the sky.

TEXT CONTINUED ON PAGE 144

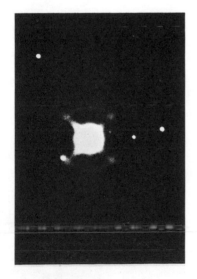

Herschel was a famous organist when he discovered Uranus (above) and abandoned music for astronomy. Then, with a grant of two hundred pounds a year from King George III he continued his researches, using the huge telescopes at right and left that he had designed himself.

141

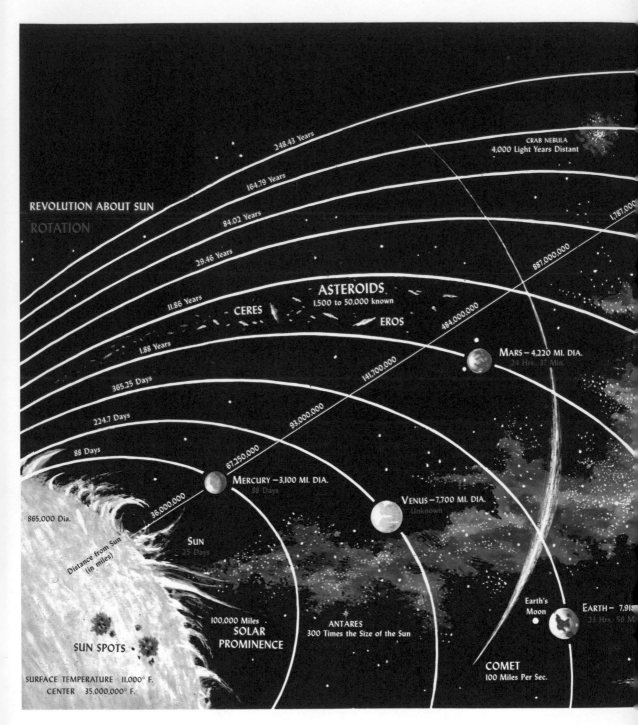

REVOLUTION ABOUT SUN

ROTATION

248.43 Years

164.79 Years

84.02 Years

29.46 Years

11.86 Years

1.88 Years

365.25 Days

224.7 Days

88 Days

CRAB NEBULA
4,000 Light Years Distant

1,787,000,000

887,000,000

ASTEROIDS
1,500 to 50,000 known

CERES

EROS

484,000,000

MARS – 4,220 MI. DIA.
24 Hrs. 37 Min.

141,700,000

93,000,000

67,250,000

36,000,000

MERCURY – 3,100 MI. DIA.
88 Days

VENUS – 7,700 MI. DIA.
Unknown

865,000 Dia.

Distance from Sun
(in miles)

SUN
25 Days

Earth's
Moon

EARTH – 7,91
23 Hrs. 56 M

SUN SPOTS

100,000 Miles
SOLAR
PROMINENCE

ANTARES
300 Times the Size of the Sun

COMET
100 Miles Per Sec.

SURFACE TEMPERATURE 11,000° F.
CENTER   35,000,000° F.

Galileo and Newton would find this modern diagram of the solar system difficult to recognize, for the three outermost planets—Uranus, Neptune, and Pluto—and the thousands of asteroids have been charted only since Newton's death. Yet modern astronomy results from the work of these two great men. Astronomers of today, using powerful instruments based on New-

3,675,000,000

,000,000

MILKY WAY GALAXY
120,000 Light Years Diameter

3,600 MI. DIA.

PLUTO   Unknown

URANUS
32,000 MI. DIA.
10 Hrs. 40 Min.

NEPTUNE
31,000 MI. DIA.
15 Hrs. 40 Min.

JUPITER — 88,700 MI. DIA.
9 Hrs. 55 Min.

SATURN — 71,600 MI. DIA.
10 Hrs. 14 Min.

ANDROMEDA GALAXY
1,500,000 Light Years
Distant

SATURN
Rings 41,500 Miles Wide

ton's optics, are studying galaxies so far away that the distances have to
be measured in light years—that is, the distance light travels in one
year, or 5,880 billion miles. And in the not-too-distant future, astronomers will be able to scan the universe even more clearly from stations on
the very planets that Galileo was the first man to understand and describe.

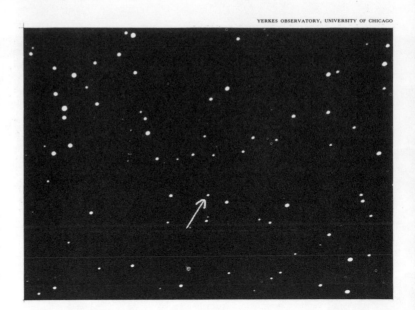

Pinpointed by the arrow in the picture at right is Pluto, the most recently discovered planet. It is named for the Greek god of Hades. Some astronomers believe that still a tenth planet exists beyond Pluto.

TEXT CONTINUED FROM PAGE 141

On September 23, 1846, the telescope in the Berlin observatory was turned in the direction that Leverrier had indicated, and that very night, within one degree of the position the Frenchman had predicted, a new planet was sighted. It was named Neptune.

When news of this discovery spread around the world, there was little doubt in scientists' minds that Newton's gravitational law was valid throughout the universe. After calculations were completed, it was found that Neptune was so far from the sun that 164 years were required to complete one revolution. And even when Neptune's orbit turned out to have unusual perturbations, no one claimed that Newton's work was in doubt. Obviously, still another planet lay in the heavens, its location known but unproven.

So the search for the newest member of the solar family began. But, although a ninth planet was known to exist, it did not prove easy to find. Some eighty years were to pass before it was finally located.

Several astronomers worked out the position of the new planet. One was William Henry Pickering. Pickering was born in Boston, Massachusetts, in 1858, and he graduated from the Massachusetts Institute of Technology in 1879. Shortly afterward, he joined his brother Edward, also a professional astronomer, in founding an observatory in Peru. Later he returned to the United States, and in 1899 discovered the ninth satellite of Saturn.

In 1919, Pickering predicted the position of the mysterious ninth planet in an article published in the *Harvard Annals*. He based his calculations on the motion of Neptune. Fourteen years earlier, a similar prediction regarding the ninth planet had been made by another astronomer who based his work on the perturbations of Uranus. His name was Percival Lowell.

Percival Lowell was also born in Boston, three years before Pickering. He came from a brilliant and wealthy family and graduated from Harvard in 1876. He began his career as a diplomat, serving for ten years in the Far East; when the so-called canals of Mars were discovered in the 1890's, his interest in astronomy began. Determined to start his own observatory to study planetary motions, he called in Pickering to build it for him.

Lowell published his prediction of the new planet in 1905. Then he began a careful search of the heavens, using photographs. Astronomers now agree that it was this painstaking work, as much as anything, that led to the discovery of Pluto. It was finally identified in February, 1930, by Clyde Tombaugh, an assistant working at Lowell's observatory. Tombaugh was studying a series of photographs taken in the previous month when he noticed that the movement of one of the heavenly bodies matched the predicted orbit of Pluto. The long search was over.

Today Pluto is still an unknown planet. It is so far away and so faint that no one has been able to tell even how large it is. And some of the mysteries that surround it have led astronomers to believe that there may be still one more planet beyond it. The process of observing its actual motions and checking them against Newtonian calculations and other theoretical data has only begun.

It is a rare event in history for the location of an unknown planet to be accurately predicted. Yet it has frequently occurred that other discoveries, perhaps not so sensational, but no less remarkable to the scientific mind, have come to light because of Newton's all-encompassing concept of the universe. Newton, for example, was able to apply his own laws to calculate the mass of the earth, the moon, the sun, and the then-known planets. And after Newton's death in 1727, the mass of the solar system in which the earth moves was finally determined; it proved to be nearly twice as large as had been expected. From this knowledge came the realization that space—the vast region lying between the planets—is not a void. Rather, space contains quantities of diffused particles of solid matter and invisible gases that account for nearly half of the volume

Percival Lowell (1855–1916) was the first to calculate Pluto's location. It was finally identified by astronomers in 1930 at the observatory he founded in Arizona.

of the solar system and which contribute to its balance.

These asteroids and gas islands were not known to either Galileo or Newton; neither, indeed, was the universe as modern scientists speak of it. The solar system's position in its own galaxy (on the fringes of the Milky Way) and the dynamic relationship of this galaxy to other swirling masses of light are concepts that have been worked out only in the last century.

Throughout most of history, the universe was regarded as the mysterious creation of God. When Newton's principles became known, scientists tended to respect the universe as though it were a precision instrument, all of whose delicately engineered workings were known. To them the universe was like a huge clock that would never run down. This concept proved to have wide appeal, and many men used it to substantiate their atheism. Others developed peculiar philosophies of their own, misapplying science to establish false proofs. Arguments developed between scientific and religious factions. In the nineteenth century, often called the mechanistic age, it was frequently considered very modern to be on the side of science—against religion.

This was certainly not Newton's point. Like Galileo, he became more and more firm in his belief in God with each revelation of the wonder of nature. For Newton, the mechanistic universe—the giant clock that kept time precisely and ran without ending—was an argument against atheism. His belief in God was absolute, and the God he believed in was "eternal and infinite; He is not duration and space, but He endures and is present." Men like Galileo and Newton recognized instinctively that science has a limited claim on men. It does not limit or control those areas of man's nature that are concerned with esthetics, morals, ethics, or religion. Galileo, as a man of the late Renaissance, was not only a scientist but an accomplished painter and musician. Newton in his last years remained influential in scientific circles, but he also devoted most of his time to theology.

Science, though limited, continues to answer the hows and whys of the universe. Yet it can only relate to ques-

Scientists used Newton's calculations to determine the amount of thrust this Saturn rocket would need to blast free of the earth's atmosphere. The Saturn is being used to launch devices that transmit back to scientists on earth astronomical data that can not be obtained from the earth's surface.

tions that may be observed in nature. A relevant example of how imaginative men can subvert science was displayed soon after Newton had published his *Principia*. Some men were not content with Newton's explanation of why things moved. They wanted to probe further, to learn why gravity existed. To this request, Newton promptly replied: "I have not been able to discover the cause of those properties of gravity from phenomena [observed occurrences] and I frame no hypothesis . . . it is enough that gravity does really exist and act according to the laws which we have explained . . ."

Newton was ever aware that what could not be observed could not be measured. And what could not be measured could not lend itself to experiment. And if it could not be made to undergo experiment, it could never become part of scientific fact. For Newton, as for Galileo before him, science began and ended with experiment.

The Hale telescope (left) at Palomar Observatory, California, is the largest in the world—the mirror alone weighs sixteen tons—while the newest solar telescope at Kitt Peak, Arizona (above), is the longest. It is housed in a tunnel slanting down three hundred feet into the mountain. Yet, with all their size and modern design, both are based on Newton's optical discoveries.

In a detail from a nineteenth-century painting, Galileo lectures on the marvels of the physical world.

ACKNOWLEDGMENTS

AMERICAN HERITAGE PUBLISHING CO., INC.

James Parton, *President*

Joseph J. Thorndike, Jr., *Editorial Director*

Richard M. Ketchum, *Editor, Book Division*

Irwin Glusker, *Art Director*

HORIZON CARAVEL BOOKS

RUSSELL BOURNE, *Managing Editor*

Janet Czarnetzki, *Art Director*

Mervyn Kaufman, *Associate Editor*

Judith Harkison, *Chief Picture Researcher*

Lucy Davidson Rosenfeld, *Picture Researcher*

Elaine K. Andrews, *Copy Editor*

Nancy Simon, *Editorial Assistant*

Betsy Sanders, *Editorial Assistant*

Gertrudis Feliu, *Chief, European Bureau*

The Editors are deeply indebted to the staff members of many private and public collections in which paintings, photographs, and articles of special importance to this book were found. Foremost among these collections are the New York Public Library; the Museo della Storia della Scienza and the Museo di Fisica e Storia Naturale in Florence, Italy; The Royal Society, Trinity College of Cambridge University; and the British Museum of London. In addition, the Editors wish to thank the following individuals and organizations for their assistance and for making available material in their collections:

The Master and Fellows, especially Professor C. D. Broad, for permission to take special photography; Dr. R. Dodwell, Wren Librarian; and A. Halcrow, College Library—Trinity College, Cambridge University

I. Kaye, Librarian—The Royal Society, London

Department of Prints and Drawings, Department of Printed Books, and Map Room—British Museum

Prints Division, Rare Book Division—New York Public Library

Burndy Library, Norwalk, Connecticut

Museo della Specola, Facolta delle Scienze Naturali dell'Universita, Florence

M. A. Cecil, Assistant to the Director—The Wallace Collection, London

Mary Pettman—National Portrait Gallery, London

Bodleian Library, University Press and New College—Oxford

Fitzwilliam Museum and University Library—Cambridge

The Science Museum, London

Silvio Bedini, Museum of History and Technology, Smithsonian Institution

Special research and photography: Italy—Maria Todorow, Fiorella Ginanneschi, Ann Natanson, Societa Scala; France—Claire de Forbin; England—Susanne Puddefoot, Christopher Angeloglou, John R. Freeman, Zoltan Wegner, Stanley A. R. Eost, and the British Museum Photographic Studio

Map and drawings by Herbert Borst

FURTHER REFERENCE

Readers interested in further examining astronomical and scientific instruments pertaining to the times of Galileo and Newton will find collections of varying kinds in the following museums: Adler Planetarium and Astronomical Museum, Chicago; Museum of History and Technology, Smithsonian Institution; Peabody Museum, Salem, Mass.; Los Angeles County Museum; and The Metropolitan Museum of Art, New York City. For astronomical shows, lectures, and exhibits, the following major planetariums are open to the public: American Museum-Hayden Planetarium, New York City; Buhl Planetarium, Pittsburgh; Fels Planetarium, Philadelphia; Griffith Observatory and Planetarium, Los Angeles; Kansas City Museum and Planetarium; Morehead Planetarium, Chapel Hill, N.C.; Adler Planetarium, Chicago.

For those who wish to read more about Galileo and Newton and their scientific achievements, the following books are recommended:

Anthony, H. D. *Sir Isaac Newton*. Abelard-Schuman, 1960.

Armitage, Angus. *The World of Copernicus*. Mentor Books, 1951.

Brophy, James, and Paolucci, Henry, Eds. *The Achievement of Galileo*. Twayne Publishers, 1962.

Butterfield, Herbert. *The Origins of Modern Science*. Collier Books, 1957.

Cooper, L. *Aristotle, Galileo and the Tower of Pisa*. Cornell Univ. Press, 1935.

Cowan, Harrison J. *Time and Its Measurement*. The World Publishing Co., 1958.

Crombie, A. C. *Medieval and Modern Science*. Vol. II. Doubleday Anchor Books, 1959.

De Santillana, Giorgio. *The Crime of Galileo*. Univ. of Chicago Press, 1955.

De Santillana, Giorgio, Ed. *Dialogue of the Great World Systems*. Univ. of Chicago Press, 1953.

Hall, A. Rupert. *From Galileo to Newton: 1630–1720*. Harper & Row, 1963.

More, Louis T. *Isaac Newton*. Dover Publications, 1934.

Namer, Émile *Galileo, Searcher of the Heavens*. Robert M. McBride & Co., 1931.

Pledge, H. T. *Science Since 1500*. Harper & Row, 1959.

Reichen, Charles-Albert. *A History of Astronomy*. Hawthorn Books, 1963.

Reichen, Charles-Albert. *A History of Physics*. Hawthorn Books, 1963.

Sarton, George. *Six Wings, Men of Science in the Renaissance*. Indiana Univ. Press, 1957.

Sarton, George. *The History of Science and the New Humanism*. Harvard Univ. Press, 1937.

Stillman, Drake, Ed. *Discoveries and Opinions of Galileo*. Doubleday Anchor Books, 1957.

Struik, Dirk. *A Concise History of Mathematics*. Dover Publications, 1948.

Thiel, Rudolf. *And There Was Light*. Alfred A. Knopf, 1957.

Turnbull, A. W., Ed. *The Correspondence of Isaac Newton*. 3 vols. Cambridge Univ. Press, 1959–1961.

INDEX

Bold face indicates pages on which maps or illustrations appear